PRENTICE HALL

SCIENCE EXPLORER

Focus on
Earth Science
Student Edition

Guided Reading and Study Workbook

CALIFORNIA EDITION

Prentice Hall

PRENTICE HALL
Needham, Massachusetts
Upper Saddle River, New Jersey
Glenview, Illinois

Student Edition ISBN 0-13-052727-0
1 2 3 4 5 6 7 8 9 10   06 05 04 03 02 01 00

Table of Contents

TABLE OF CONTENTS *(continued)*

CHAPTER 1

PLATE TECTONICS

....

SECTION 1–1 **Earth's Interior**
(pages 6-14)

This section explains how scientists learn about Earth's interior. The section also describes the layers that make up Earth and explains why Earth acts like a giant magnet.

▶ The Science of Geology (pages 7–8)

1. Earth's hard surface is formed of _____.

2. The study of planet Earth is called _____.

3. What did geologists of the late 1700s conclude about Earth's landforms?

_____

_____

4. Is the following sentence true or false? Earth looks the same today as it

did millions of years ago. _____

5. What is the difference between constructive and destructive forces? Give an

example of each. _____

_____

_____

6. Circle the letter of each sentence that is true about Earth.

   a. Earth has five great landmasses, called continents.

   b. Geologists cannot observe Earth's interior directly.

   c. It is over 6,000 kilometers from the surface to the center of Earth.

   d. Geologists learn about Earth's interior by digging holes.

CHAPTER 1, Plate Tectonics *(continued)*

7. _____ waves are produced by earthquakes.

▶ A Journey to the Center of the Earth (page 9)

8. How does the temperature change as you go from the surface toward the

   center of Earth? _____

   _____

9. How does pressure change as you go from the surface toward the center

   of Earth? _____

10. The three main layers that make up Earth's interior are the

    _____, _____, and _____.

▶ The Crust (page 10)

11. The _____ is a layer of rock that forms Earth's outer skin.

12. Is the following sentence true or false? The crust is thinnest under high

    mountains. _____

13. The dark-colored rock that makes up most of the oceanic crust is

    _____.

14. The light-colored rock that makes up most of the continental crust is

    _____.

▶ The Mantle (pages 10–11)

Match the name of each layer of Earth with its description.

Layer	Description
_____ 15. mantle	**a.** Rigid layer that includes the upper part of the mantle and the crust
_____ 16. lithosphere	**b.** Layer of hot rock between the crust and the core
_____ 17. asthenosphere	**c.** Soft layer just below the lithosphere

© Prentice-Hall, Inc.

18. Is the following sentence true or false? The asthenosphere floats on the lithosphere. _____

19. Is the following sentence true or false? The mantle is nearly 3,000 kilometers thick. _____

▶ The Core (pages 11–13)

20. Circle the letter of each sentence that is true about Earth's outer core.

   a. It makes up about 25 percent of Earth's total volume.

   b. It is made of solid metal.

   c. It contains iron and nickel.

   d. It behaves like a solid.

21. Circle the letter of each sentence that is true about Earth's inner core.

   a. It consists of molten metal.

   b. It behaves like a thick liquid.

   c. It is not very dense.

   d. It is under extreme pressure.

22. In the drawing, label the three main layers of Earth.

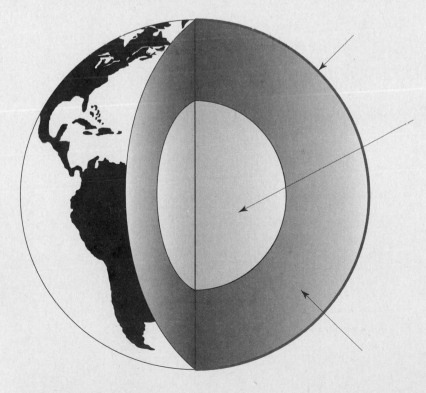

CHAPTER 1, Plate Tectonics *(continued)*

▶ Earth's Magnetic Field (page 14)

23. What forces Earth's solid inner core to spin? _____

_____

24. What creates Earth's magnetic field? _____

_____

· ·

SECTION 1-2 Convection Currents and the Mantle
(pages 15-17)

This section describes how heat is transferred from Earth's hot core through the mantle.

▶ Introduction (page 15)

1. The movement of energy from a warmer object to a cooler object is

   called _____.

2. List the three types of heat transfer.

   a. _____   b. _____   c. _____

▶ Radiation (page 15)

3. What is radiation? _____

_____

4. What are two forms of radiation? _____

_____

▶ Conduction (page 16)

5. What is conduction? _____

_____

6. What is an example of conduction? _____

_____

▶ Convection (pages 16–17)

7. What is convection? _____

_____

8. Heat transfer by convection is caused by differences of _____ and density within a fluid.

9. A measure of how much mass there is in a volume of a substance is

_____.

10. Circle the letter of the sentence that describes what happens to a fluid when its temperature increases.

   a. Its particles occupy less space.

   b. Its density decreases.

   c. Its particles move more slowly.

   d. Its particles settle together more closely.

11. Use arrows to show the convection currents that would flow if the pot of soup in the drawing was heated.

12. If the pot is no longer heated, when will the convection currents stop

   flowing? _____

_____

▶ Convection in Earth's Mantle (page 17)

13. Is the following sentence true or false? Convection currents flow in the

   asthenosphere. _____

14. Is the following sentence true or false? The heat source for the

   convection currents in the mantle is the sun. _____

CHAPTER 1, Plate Tectonics *(continued)*

• •

Drifting Continents
(pages 18-22)

This section describes a theory of how the continents came to be located where they are today. The section also gives evidence for the theory and explains why the theory was not accepted for many years.

▶ The Theory of Continental Drift (pages 19–21)

1. State Alfred Wegener's hypothesis about how Earth's continents have moved.

_____

_____

_____

2. Wegener named his supercontinent _____.

3. What did Wegener think had happened to this supercontinent?

_____

_____

_____

4. Wegener's idea that the continents slowly moved over Earth's surface

became known as _____.

5. Complete the concept map.

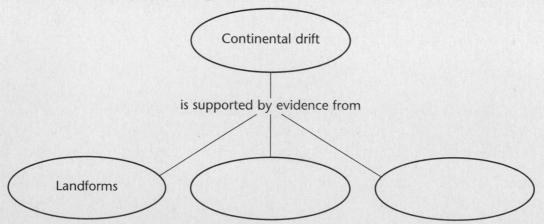

6. Give an example of evidence from landforms that supported Wegener's idea of continental drift. _____

_____

_____

7. Any trace of an ancient organism preserved in rock is called a(n)

_____.

8. How did Wegener explain similar fossils on different continents?

_____

_____

9. Is the following sentence true or false? Wegener believed that Earth's climate had changed. _____

▶ **Scientists Reject Wegener's Theory** (page 22)

10. How did Wegener think that mountains formed? _____

_____

_____

11. How do the locations of mountains support Wegener's idea about how mountains form? _____

_____

_____

📖 Reading Skill Practice

When you read about a complex subject, taking notes can help you to identify the most important information. Take notes on Section 1–3 by writing down the headings in the order they occur. Then, under each heading, list the main points. Do your work on a separate sheet of paper.

CHAPTER 1, Plate Tectonics *(continued)*

Sea-Floor Spreading
(pages 23–29)

This section explains sea-floor spreading and describes evidence that it happens. The section also explains subduction and describes how subduction affects Earth's oceans.

▶ **Mapping the Mid-Ocean Ridge** (page 24)

1. Circle the letter of each sentence that is true about the mid-ocean ridge.

   a. The mid-ocean ridge is the longest chain of mountains in the world.

   b. The mid-ocean ridge is found only below the Pacific Ocean.

   c. The mid-ocean ridge lies completely under water.

   d. The top of the mid-ocean ridge is split by a steep-sided valley.

2. A device that bounces sound waves off underwater objects is called

   _____.

3. What is sonar used for? _____

   _____

▶ **Evidence for Sea-Floor Spreading** (pages 25–27)

4. The process that continually adds new material to the ocean floor is

   called _____.

5. Complete the cycle diagram of sea-floor spreading.

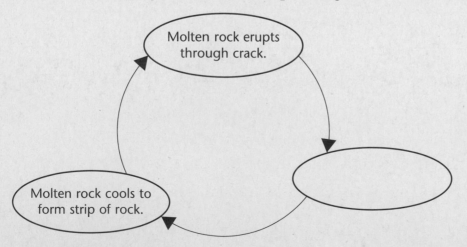

6. List three types of evidence for sea-floor spreading.

a. _____ b. _____ c. _____

7. Circle the letter of each sentence that is true about Earth's magnetism.

   a. At times in the past, a compass needle on Earth would have pointed south.

   b. Rock that makes up the ocean floor lies in a pattern of magnetized stripes.

   c. The pattern of stripes is different on both sides of the mid-ocean ridge.

   d. Rocks that harden at the same time have the same "magnetic memory."

8. How did drilling samples show that sea-floor spreading really has taken

place? _____

_____

_____

▶ **Subduction at Deep-Ocean Trenches** (page 28)

9. Deep underwater canyons are called _____.

10. What is subduction? _____

_____

11. Is the following sentence true or false? At deep-ocean trenches, conduction allows oceanic crust to sink back into the mantle.

_____

▶ **Subduction and Earth's Oceans** (page 29)

12. Is the following statement true or false? The Pacific Ocean is shrinking.

_____

13. Why is the Atlantic Ocean expanding? _____

_____

_____

CHAPTER 1, Plate Tectonics *(continued)*

© Prentice-Hall, Inc.

SECTION 1–5 **The Theory of Plate Tectonics**
(pages 32–37)

This section explains how the lithosphere is broken into separate sections that move.

▶ **Introduction** (page 32)

1. The lithosphere is broken into separate sections called _____.

2. Is the following sentence true or false? Plates can carry continents or parts of the ocean floor but not both. _____

▶ **A Theory of Plate Motion** (page 33)

3. What is a scientific theory? _____

_____

4. State the theory of plate tectonics. _____

_____

_____

5. Is the following sentence true or false? The theory of plate tectonics explains the formation, movement, and subduction of Earth's plates.

_____

▶ **Plate Boundaries** (pages 34–36)

Match the term with its definition.

Term	Definition
_____ **6.** plate boundary	**a.** Deep valley that forms where two plates pull apart
_____ **7.** fault	**b.** Line where different pieces of the lithosphere meet
_____ **8.** rift valley	**c.** Break in Earth's crust where rocks have slipped past each other

9. Complete the table.

Plate Movement	
Type of Plate Boundary	**How Plates Move**
Transform boundary	
Divergent boundary	
Convergent boundary	

10. Is the following sentence true or false? Crust is both created and destroycd along a transform boundary. _____

11. Most divergent boundaries occur at the _____.

12. When two plates converge, the result is called a(n) _____.

13. When two plates collide, what determines which plate comes out on top?

_____

_____

14. Complete the table.

Convergent Boundaries	
Types of Plates Converging	**Result**
	Subduction occurs.
Oceanic/continental	
	Mountain ranges form.

▶ The Continents' Slow Dance (page 37)

15. About how fast do plates move? _____

_____

16. Is the following sentence true or false? The pieces of the super continent Pangea began to drift apart about 225 million years ago.

_____

CHAPTER 1, Plate Tectonics (continued)

WordWise

Use key terms from Chapter 1 to complete the crossword puzzle.

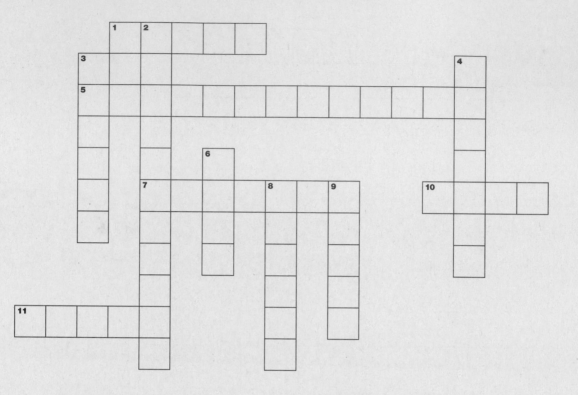

Clues across

1. Section of lithosphere that carries crust
5. Part of mantle below lithosphere
7. Kind of wave released during an earthquake
10. Forms Earth's hard surface
11. Used to map mid-ocean ridge

Clues down

2. Layer that is part crust and part mantle
3. Rock that makes up oceanic crust
4. Study of planet Earth
6. Kind of valley where plates move apart
8. Earth's middle layer
9. Earth's outer layer

Science Explorer *Focus on Earth Science*

CHAPTER 2

EARTHQUAKES

· ·

SECTION 2–1 Earth's Crust in Motion (pages 44–51)

This section explains how stresses in Earth's crust cause breaks in the crust called faults. The section also explains how faults and folds in Earth's crust form mountains.

▶ Stress in the Crust (page 44)

1. The shaking and trembling that results from the movement of rock

   beneath Earth's surface is called a(n) _____.

2. Circle the letter of the term that refers to force that acts on rock to
   change its shape or volume.

   a. fault   **b.** stress   **c.** pressure   **d.** heat

▶ Types of Stress (page 45)

3. List the three types of stress that occur in Earth's crust.

   a. _____ b. _____ c. _____

4. Define shearing, and describe how it can affect rock. _____

   _____

   _____

   _____

5. Define tension, and describe how it can affect rock. _____

   _____

   _____

   _____

Name _____ Date _____ Class _____

CHAPTER 2, Earthquakes *(continued)*

6. Define compression, and describe how it can affect rock. _____

_____

_____

7. Circle the letter of the term that means any change in the volume or shape of Earth's crust.

a. deformation   **b.** compression   **c.** tension   **d.** stress

▶ Kinds of Faults (pages 46–47)

8. A break in Earth's crust is a(n) _____.

Match the kind of fault with its description.

Kind of Fault

_____ **9.** strike-slip fault

_____ **10.** normal fault

_____ **11.** reverse fault

Description

a. The hanging wall slides up and over the footwall.

b. There is little up or down motion.

c. The hanging wall slips downward below the footwall.

12. Is the following sentence true or false? A strike-slip fault that forms the boundary between two plates is called a convergent boundary.

_____

13. Circle the letter of each sentence that is true about a hanging wall.

a. It is the half of a fault that lies above the fault.

b. It is the half of a fault that lies below the fault.

c. It is the same as a footwall.

d. It occurs when the fault is at an angle.

14. Circle the letter of each sentence that is true about both normal and reverse faults.

a. The faults are at an angle.   **b.** The faults are caused by tension.

c. The faults are caused by compression.   **d.** The faults have footwalls.

15. Complete the flowchart.

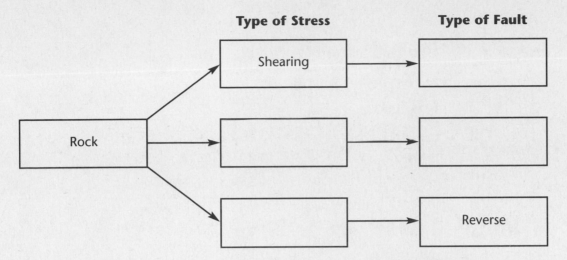

Match the landform with the type of fault that produced it.

Landform

_____ **16.** San Andreas Fault

_____ **17.** Rio Grande Valley

_____ **18.** Appalachian Mountains

Type of Fault

a. reverse fault

b. strike-slip fault

c. normal fault

▶ Friction Along Faults (page 48)

19. The force that opposes the motion of one surface as it moves across

another surface is referred to as _____.

▶ Mountain Building (pages 48–51)

20. Circle the letter of the sentence that describes how a fault-block
mountain is created.

a. It is created by two normal faults.

b. It is created by two reverse faults.

c. It is created by a strike-slip fault.

d. It is created by shearing.

21. Circle the letter of each mountain range that was caused by folding.

a. Alps   **b.** Himalayas   **c.** Tetons   **d.** Sierra Nevadas

CHAPTER 2, Earthquakes *(continued)*

Match the term with its definition.

Term	Definition
_____ 22. anticline	**a.** Fold in rock that bends upward
_____ 23. syncline	**b.** Large area of flat land high above sea level
_____ 24. plateau	**c.** Fold in rock that bends downward

📖 Reading Skill Practice

When reading about related processes, drawings can help you appreciate their similarities and differences. Study Figures 3, 4, and 5 in Section 2-1 and explain how the figures are similar and how they are different. Do your work on a separate sheet of paper.

SECTION 2–2

Measuring Earthquakes
(pages 54–59)

This section explains how energy from an earthquake can be detected and how the size of an earthquake can be measured.

▶ Introduction (page 54)

1. The point where a rock under stress breaks and triggers an earthquake is

   called the _____.

2. The point on the surface directly above the focus is the _____.

▶ Seismic Waves (pages 54–56)

3. What are seismic waves? _____

   _____

   _____

Science Explorer *Focus on Earth Science*

4. Is the following sentence true or false? Seismic waves carry the energy of

an earthquake away from the focus in all directions. _____

5. Circle the letter of each term that is a category of seismic wave.

    a. P wave   **b.** S wave

    c. surface wave   **d.** underground wave

6. Label each drawing as *S Waves* or *P Waves*.

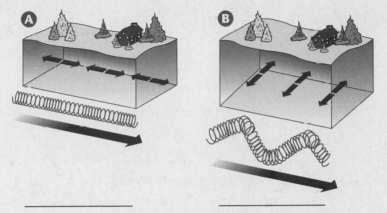

_____

7. Is the following sentence true or false? Surface waves move more quickly

than P waves and S waves. _____

▶ Detecting Seismic Waves (page 56)

8. A device that records the ground movements caused by seismic waves is

a(n) _____.

▶ Measuring Earthquakes (pages 57–58)

9. List the three scales that are used for measuring earthquakes.

    a. _____

    b. _____

    c. _____

10. Circle the letter of the term that refers to the strength of earthquakes as
measured by seismic waves and movement along faults.

    a. Richter value   **b.** magnitude

    c. Mercalli force   **d.** vibrations

CHAPTER 2, Earthquakes *(continued)*

▶ Locating the Epicenter (pages 58–59)

11. Is the following sentence true or false? The closer an earthquake, the greater the time between the arrival of P waves and the arrival of S

waves. _____

SECTION 2-3 **Earthquake Hazards and Safety**
(pages 62-67)

This section explains how earthquakes cause damage. The section also describes how buildings can be constructed to withstand earthquakes and what people can do to help protect themselves from earthquakes.

▶ How Earthquakes Cause Damage (pages 63–64)

1. What kinds of damage are caused by the severe shaking of an earthquake?

_____

_____

2. Is the following sentence true or false? The thicker the layer of soil, the

more violent the shaking will be during an earthquake. _____

3. Is the following sentence true or false? A house built on solid rock will shake more during an earthquake than a house built on sandy soil.

_____

4. When an earthquake's violent shaking turns loose, soft soil into liquid

mud, it is called _____. It is likely where the soil is full of

_____. It can trigger _____.

5. An earthquake that occurs after a larger earthquake in the same area is

referred to as a(n) _____.

6. Large waves caused by strong earthquakes on the ocean floor are called

_____.

▶ Making Buildings Safer (pages 64–67)

7. How can a building's location affect the type of damage it may suffer

during an earthquake? _____

_____

_____

8. Is the following sentence true or false? The farther a structure is from a

fault, the stronger the shaking will be. _____

9. How can a brick or wood-frame building be modified to help it

withstand an earthquake? _____

_____

10. What can be done when a new home is being built to help prevent

damage caused by liquefaction? _____

_____

_____

11. Complete the table below.

Buildings and Earthquakes		
Type of Building	**What It Rests On**	**How It Moves During an Earthquake**
	Foundation	Tilts and cracks
Base-isolated		

12. How can earthquakes cause fire and flooding? _____

_____

_____

CHAPTER 2, Earthquakes *(continued)*

▶ Protecting Yourself During an Earthquake (page 67)

13. What is the main danger to people during an earthquake? _____

_____

14. Is the following sentence true or false? If no desk or table is available,

you should crouch against an outside wall. _____

15. Is the following sentence true or false? If you are outdoors during an

earthquake, you should move under a tree or building. _____

SECTION 2-4 **Monitoring Faults** (pages 68-71)

This section explains how geologists monitor faults to try to predict earthquakes.

▶ Devices that Monitor Faults (pages 69–70)

1. Is the following sentence true or false? To predict earthquakes,
geologists measure stress and deformation in the crust along faults.

_____

2. List four instruments that geologists use to monitor movements along
faults.

a. _____ b. _____

c. _____ d. _____

Match the type of monitoring device with its description.

Type of Monitoring Device	Description
_____ **3.** creep meter	**a.** Uses radar to make images of faults
_____ **4.** laser-ranging device	**b.** Detects changes in distance to a reflector
_____ **5.** tiltmeter	**c.** Measures movement along a slip-strike fault
_____ **6.** satellite monitor	**d.** Works like a carpenter's level

© Prentice-Hall, Inc.

7. Label each circle in the Venn diagram with the name of the monitoring device it represents.

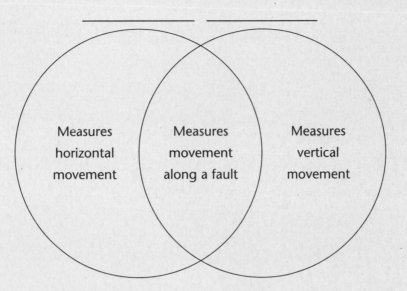

8. A device that bounces laser beams off a reflector to detect fault movements is a(n) _____.

9. A device that bounces radio waves off the ground to detect changes in elevation is a(n) _____.

▶ Monitoring Risk in the United States (pages 70–71)

10. Is the following sentence true or false? Geologists can predict accurately where and when an earthquake will strike. _____

11. What two factors do geologists take into account when they determine earthquake risk? _____

_____

_____

12. Circle the letter of the location where the risk of earthquakes is highest in the United States.

    a. along the Gulf of Mexico   **b.** along the Atlantic coast

    c. along the Great Lakes   **d.** along the Pacific coast

CHAPTER 2, Earthquakes *(continued)*

WordWise

Read the clues below, and then find the key terms from Chapter 2 that are hidden in the puzzle. The hidden terms may occur vertically, horizontally, or diagonally.

Clues

1. The shaking and trembling of Earth's crust

2. A fold in rock that bends downward

3. A stress force that squeezes rock

4. A large area of elevated flat land

5. A force that changes rock's shape or volume

6. Any change in the volume or shape of Earth's crust

7. Large waves caused by earthquakes on the ocean floor

8. Stress that pushes rock in opposite directions

9. A fold in rock that bends upward

10. Occurs when an earthquake turns soil into liquid mud

11. The half of a fault that lies below

12. An instrument that records ground movements caused by seismic waves

```
s  t  i  o  n  s  c  o  d  d  l  n  p  m
f  a  e  a  r  t  h  q  u  a  k  e  v  l
w  d  e  f  o  r  m  a  t  i  o  n  d  i
y  t  o  n  e  e  q  u  r  c  a  f  t  q
d  u  p  c  o  s  h  e  a  r  i  n  g  u
s  w  n  o  f  s  a  z  s  e  p  t  w  e
e  g  o  m  i  p  h  o  r  v  a  d  t  f
i  n  m  p  f  g  t  p  u  l  a  c  m  a
s  o  d  r  s  y  n  c  l  i  n  e  p  c
m  w  c  e  o  m  u  a  q  a  v  b  c  t
o  v  e  s  j  m  w  u  c  k  t  i  b  i
g  l  n  s  o  t  h  u  m  b  b  e  y  o
r  a  t  i  o  k  v  o  o  x  l  e  a  n
a  w  o  o  p  l  y  i  m  s  s  a  h  u
p  u  f  n  t  t  s  u  n  a  m  i  s  s
h  a  l  e  t  a  n  t  i  c  l  i  n  e
```

CHAPTER 3

VOLCANOES

● ●

SECTION 3-1 | Volcanoes and Plate Tectonics (pages 78-81)

This section explains what volcanoes are and identifies where most volcanoes occur.

▶ What Is a Volcano? (page 78)

1. What is a volcano? _____

_____

_____

2. A molten mixture of rock-forming substances, gases, and water from the

mantle is referred to as _____.

3. When magma reaches the surface, it is called _____.

▶ Location of Volcanoes (page 79)

4. What is the Ring of Fire? _____

_____

_____

5. Complete the concept map.

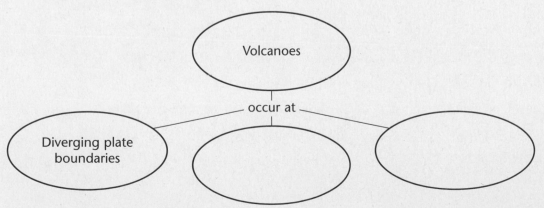

CHAPTER 3, Volcanoes *(continued)*

▶ Volcanoes at Diverging Plate Boundaries (page 79)

6. Describe how volcanoes form along the mid-ocean ridge. _____

_____

_____

7. Is the following sentence true or false? Most volcanoes of the mid-ocean ridge rise above the ocean's surface. _____

▶ Volcanoes at Converging Boundaries (page 80)

8. Is the following sentence true or false? Many volcanoes form near converging plate boundaries where oceanic crust returns to the mantle.

_____

9. How does subduction at converging plate boundaries lead to the formation of volcanoes? _____

_____

_____

_____

10. Volcanoes at boundaries where two oceanic plates collide create a string of islands called a(n) _____.

11. What are three major island arcs? _____

_____

_____

12. Circle the letter of the types of plates that collided to form the Andes Mountains on the west coast of South America.

    a. two oceanic plates   **c.** a continental plate and an oceanic plate

    b. a continental plate and an island plate   **d.** two continental plates

▶ Hot Spot Volcanoes (page 81)

13. What is a hot spot? _____

_____

_____

14. How did the Hawaiian Islands form? _____

_____

15. Is the following sentence true or false? Hot spots form only under

oceanic crust. _____

Reading Skill Practice

When you read detailed information, writing a summary can help you identify and remember the main ideas. Write a concise paragraph summing up the main ideas under each heading In Section 3-1. Try to use each of the boldfaced terms in your summary. Do your work on a separate sheet of paper.

SECTION 3-2

Volcanic Activity
(pages 83-92)

This section explains how volcanoes erupt and describes types of volcanic eruptions as well as other types of volcanic activity. The section also describes how geologists monitor volcanoes and what hazards are associated with volcanoes.

▶ How Magma Reaches Earth's Surface (pages 83–84)

1. Is the following sentence true or false? Magma forms in the lithosphere.

_____

2. Is the following sentence true or false? Liquid magma rises until it reaches the surface or until it becomes trapped beneath layers of rock.

_____

CHAPTER 3, Volcanoes *(continued)*

3. Circle the letter of the sentence that describes the best model of a volcano erupting.

   a. Carbon dioxide dissolved in soda pop rushes out when the pop is opened.

   b. A car goes faster when the accelerator is pushed.

   c. Water in a pot gets hotter when the pot is heated on a stove.

   d. Clay hardens when it is baked in an oven.

4. What happens during a volcanic eruption? _____

_____

_____

▶ Inside a Volcano (pages 84–85)

5. Circle the letter of each feature that all volcanoes share.

   a. pocket of magma beneath the surface   **b.** crack to the surface

   c. side vents   **d.** crater

6. Label the drawing with the following terms: magma chamber, pipe, vent, and crater.

Science Explorer *Focus on Earth Science*

7. What is a lava flow? _____

_____

8. Where does a crater form? _____

_____

9. Is the following sentence true or false? The pipe of a volcano is a

horizontal crack in the crust. _____

▶ Characteristics of Magma (page 86)

10. What factors determine the force of a volcanic eruption? _____

_____

_____

_____

11. Circle the letter of each sentence that is true about silica.

a. It is formed from oxygen and nitrogen.

b. It makes magma thicker.

c. It is rarely found in the crust.

d. It produces light-colored lava.

Match the type of rock with its description.

Type of Rock	Description
_____ **12.** rhyolite	**a.** Has the same composition as granite
_____ **13.** obsidian	**b.** Forms from low-silica lava
_____ **14.** pumice	**c.** Forms when high-silica lava cools very quickly
_____ **15.** basalt	**d.** Forms when gas bubbles are trapped in cooling lava

▶ Types of Volcanic Eruptions (pages 87–88)

16. Is the following sentence true or false? A volcano erupts quietly if its

magma is thick and sticky. _____

CHAPTER 3, Volcanoes *(continued)*

17. Hot, fast-moving lava is called _____.

18. Cool, slow-moving lava is called _____.

Match the type of lava with its description.

Type of Lava

_____ **19.** volcanic ash

_____ **20.** cinders

_____ **21.** bombs

Description

a. Pebble-sized particles

b. Particles ranging from the size of a baseball to the size of a car

c. Fine rocky particles as small as a grain of sand

22. What is a pyroclastic flow? _____

_____

_____

▶ Stages of a Volcano (page 88)

23. Is the following sentence true or false? The activity of a volcano may last from less than a decade to more than 10 million years.

_____

24. Is the following sentence true or false? Most long-lived volcanoes erupt continuously. _____

25. Complete the compare/contrast table.

Volcanic Stages	
Stage	**Description**
	Unlikely to erupt ever again
	Erupting or showing signs that it soon will erupt
	No longer active but may become active again

26. Is the following sentence true or false? The length of time between eruptions of a dormant volcano is always less than a thousand years.

_____

▶ Other Types of Volcanic Activity (page 89)

27. Is the following sentence true or false? Some types of volcanic activity do not involve the eruption of lava. _____

28. When groundwater heated by a nearby body of magma rises to the surface and collects in a natural pool, it is called a(n) _____.

29. A fountain of water and steam that erupts from the ground is referred to as a(n) _____.

30. How can geothermal energy be converted to electricity? _____

_____

_____

_____

▶ Monitoring Volcanoes (pages 90–91)

31. Circle the letter of the sentence that is true about predicting volcanic eruptions.

   a. Geologists are less successful in predicting volcanic eruptions than earthquakes.

   b. There is never any warning when a volcano will erupt.

   c. Geologists can predict how powerful a volcanic eruption will be.

   d. Geologists cannot predict what type of eruption a volcano will produce.

▶ Volcano Hazards (pages 91–92)

32. Why might people living near a dormant volcano be unaware of the

   danger? _____

_____

CHAPTER 3, Volcanoes (continued)

33. Is the following sentence true or false? Volcanic eruptions only cause

damage close to the crater's rim. _____

34. What kinds of damage can volcanoes cause? _____

_____

_____

_____

• •

SECTION 3-3 Volcanic Landforms (pages 93-97)

This section describes landforms and soils that are created by volcanoes.

▶ Landforms From Lava and Ash (pages 93–95)

1. List four landforms created from lava and ash.

a. _____ b. _____

c. _____ d. _____

2. Circle the letter of each sentence that is true about shield volcanoes.

a. They form from many thin layers of lava.

b. They result from quiet eruptions.

c. They are very steep mountains.

d. They are formed from ash, cinders, and bombs.

3. Is the following sentence true or false? The Hawaiian Islands are cinder

cone volcanoes. _____

4. Name three examples of composite volcanoes. _____

_____

5. Is the following sentence true or false? A composite volcano has both

quiet and explosive eruptions. _____

Match the landform with its description.

Landform	Description
_____ **6.** shield volcano	**a.** High, level area formed by repeated lava flows
_____ **7.** cinder cone	**b.** Mountain formed by lava flows alternating with explosive eruptions
_____ **8.** composite volcano	**c.** Cone-shaped mountain formed from ash, cinders, and bombs
_____ **9.** lava plateau	**d.** Hole left by the collapse of a volcanic mountain
_____ **10.** caldera	**e.** Gently sloping mountain formed by repeated lava flows

▶ Soils from Lava and Ash (page 96)

11. When volcanic ash breaks down, it releases _____ and

_____, both of which are needed by plants.

▶ Landforms from Magma (pages 96–97)

12. List five features formed by magma.

a. _____   c. _____   e. _____

b. _____   d. _____

13. Complete the Venn diagram using the following phrases: forms from magma, forms across rock layers, forms between rock layers.

Dike   Sill

CHAPTER 3, Volcanoes *(continued)*

14. A mass of rock formed when a large body of magma cools inside the

    crust is called a(n) _____.

15. What is an example of a batholith in the United States? _____

    _____

16. Is the following sentence true or false? A dome mountain forms when

    rising magma is blocked by horizontal layers of rock. _____

•••

SECTION 3-4 **Volcanoes in the Solar System** *(pages 100-102)*

This section describes volcanoes that occur in the solar system on moons and planets other than Earth.

▶ **Earth's Moon** (page 100)

1. The craters on the surface of Earth's moon were produced by

   _____.

2. What produced the dark, smooth areas on the surface of Earth's moon?

   _____

▶ **Volcanoes on Venus** (page 101)

3. Circle the letter of each sentence that is true about volcanoes on Venus.

   a. Geologists learned about volcanoes on Venus from the space probe *Magellan*.

   b. Venus has thousands of volcanoes.

   c. The largest volcano on Venus is 4 kilometers high.

   d. The lava that produced landforms on Venus was thick and sticky.

4. Is the following sentence true or false? Venus has long, riverlike lava

   flows. _____

▶ Volcanoes on Mars (pages 101–102)

5. How does the number of volcanoes on Mars compare with the number

   on Venus? _____

   _____

6. Circle the letter of each sentence that is true about volcanoes on Mars.

   a. Mars has a long history of volcanic activity.

   b. Mars has only cone-shaped volcanoes.

   c. Mars has lava plains like the lava flows on Earth's moon.

   d. Mars has the biggest volcanic mountain in the solar system.

7. What type of volcano is Olympus Mons? _____

   _____

8. Is the following sentence true or false? Martian volcanoes seem to be

   extremely active. _____

▶ Volcanoes on Distant Moons (page 101)

9. Is the following sentence true or false? Volcanic eruptions have actually

   been observed only on Earth, Io, and Triton. _____

10. Is the following sentence true or false? Io and Triton have volcanic
    features very similar to those on Earth, Mars, and Venus.

    _____

11. What kind of volcanoes are found on Io? _____

    _____

12. How do scientists hypothesize that volcanoes occur on Triton?

    _____

    _____

    _____

    _____

CHAPTER 3, Volcanoes *(continued)*

WordWise

Solve the clues by filling in the blanks with key terms from Chapter 3. Then write the numbered letters in the correct order to find the hidden message.

Clues	Key Terms
Molten mixture of rock-forming substances, gases, and water	_ _ _ _ _ 1 2
Bowl-shaped area that forms around a volcano's central vent	_ _ _ _ _ 3
Material found in magma that is formed from oxygen and silicon	_ _ _ _ _ _ 4
Hot, fast-moving type of lava	_ _ _ _ _ _ _ 5
Cool, slow-moving type of lava	_ _ 6
Type of hot spring that erupts as a fountain of water and steam	_ _ _ _ _ 7
Weak spot in the crust where magma has come to the surface	_ _ _ _ _ _ 8 9
Magma that reaches the surface	_ _ _ _ 10
Erupting or showing signs of erupting in the near future	_ _ _ _ _ 11
Large hole at the top of a volcano	_ _ _ _ _ 12
Unlikely to erupt again	_ _ _ _ _ _ _ 13
Mass of rock formed when magma cooled inside the crust	_ _ _ _ _ _ _ _ _ 14
Slab that forms when magma forces itself across rock layers	_ _ _ _ 15
Slab that forms when magma squeezes between layers of rock	_ _ _ _ 16

Hidden Message

___ ___ ___ ___   ___ ___ ___   ___ ___ ___ ___ ___ ___ ___ ___ ___ .
1   2   3   4   5   6   7   8   9 10 11 12 13 14 15 16

CHAPTER 4

MINERALS

....

Properties of Minerals
(pages 108–116)

This section explains what minerals are and how they can be identified.

▶ What Is a Mineral? (pages 109–111)

1. Is the following sentence true or false? Geologists have identified about

   300 minerals. _____

2. Is the following sentence true or false? About 20 minerals make up most

   of the rocks of Earth's crust. _____

3. Complete the concept map.

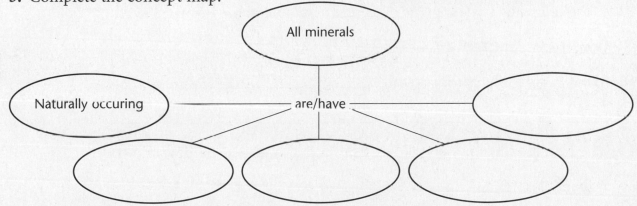

4. Because minerals do not come from living things, they are said to be

   _____.

5. A substance that keeps its shape because its particles can't flow freely is

   a(n) _____.

6. A solid with flat sides that meet at sharp edges and corners is called a(n)

   _____.

CHAPTER 4, Minerals *(continued)*

7. Is the following sentence true or false? A mineral always contains

   certain elements in definite proportions. _____

8. A substance composed of a single kind of atom is called a(n)

   _____.

9. A substance formed when two or more elements combine and lose

   their distinct properties is a(n) _____.

10. Is the following sentence true or false? Very few minerals are

    compounds. _____

11. What are some examples of minerals that occur as elements instead of

    compounds? _____

    _____

▶ **Identifying Minerals** (pages 111–116)

12. Is the following sentence true or false? Each mineral has its own specific

    properties. _____

13. What is the Mohs hardness scale? _____

    _____

14. The softest known mineral is _____. The hardest known

    mineral is _____.

15. Is the following sentence true or false? A mineral can scratch any

    mineral harder than itself. _____

16. Why can't color alone be used to identify most minerals? _____

    _____

    _____

17. The color of a mineral's powder is its _____.

18. The term that describes how a mineral reflects light from its surface is

_____.

19. Is the following sentence true or false? Minerals containing metals often

have a shiny luster. _____

20. Circle the letter of each sentence that is true about the density of a mineral.

    a. A given mineral can have varying densities.

    b. The larger the sample of a mineral, the greater its density.

    c. Each mineral has a characteristic density.

    d. The density of a mineral is its mass divided by its volume.

21. Is the following sentence true or false? Each piece of a mineral has the

same crystal structure. _____

22. How do geologists classify crystal structures? _____

_____

_____

Match the term with its definition.

Term	Definition
_____ **23.** cleavage	**a.** A mineral's ability to split easily along flat surfaces
_____ **24.** fracture	**b.** A mineral's ability to glow under ultraviolet light
_____ **25.** fluorescence	**c.** The way a mineral looks when it breaks

Reading Skill Practice

Studying a compare/contrast table can help you remember detailed information. Use the chart in Figure 8 of Section 4-1 to compare and contrast the properties of quartz and sulfur. Then write a summary of their similarities and differences. Do your work on a separate sheet of paper. For more information about compare/contrast tables, see page 720 in the Skills Handbook of your textbook.

CHAPTER 4, Minerals (continued)

SECTION 4-2 How Minerals Form
(pages 118-122)

This section describes how minerals form and where minerals are found.

▶ Processes That Form Minerals (page 119)

1. In what two ways do minerals form? _____

_____

_____

_____

2. The process by which atoms are arranged to form a material with a

crystal structure is referred to as _____.

▶ Minerals From Magma (page 119)

3. What affects the size of crystals formed from magma? _____

_____

_____

_____

4. Why does magma that cools deep below the surface have large crystals?

_____

_____

5. Is the following sentence true or false? Lava cools quickly and forms

minerals with small crystals. _____

▶ Minerals From Hot Water Solutions (pages 120–121)

6. A mixture in which one substance dissolves in another is called a(n)

_____.

7. How do minerals form from a hot water solution? _____

_____

_____

_____

8. A narrow channel or slab of a mineral that is much different from the surrounding rock is called a(n) _____.

9. How do veins form? _____

_____

_____

10. Explain how minerals form from solutions along the mid-ocean ridge.

_____

_____

_____

_____

11. Complete the Venn diagram by labeling the circles with the type of minerals they represent.

_____   _____

Form from melted materials

Form through crystallization

Form from dissolved materials

▶ Minerals Formed by Evaporation (page 121)

12. Is the following sentence true or false? Minerals can form when solutions evaporate. _____

CHAPTER 4, Minerals *(continued)*

13. Circle the letter of each sentence that is true about halite deposits in the United States.

    a. Deposits are found in the Midwest and Southwest.

    b. Deposits are found along the Gulf Coast.

    c. Deposits formed over the past thousand years.

    d. Deposits formed when ancient seas evaporated.

▶ Where Minerals Are Found (page 122)

14. What is Earth's crust mostly made up of? _____

    _____

    _____

    _____

15. Is the following sentence true or false? Uncommon minerals are

    distributed evenly throughout Earth's crust. _____

16. Is the following sentence true or false? Many valuable minerals are found in or near areas of volcanic activity and mountain building.

    _____

· ·

SECTION 4-3 Mineral Resources (pages 124–129)

This section describes the uses of minerals and how minerals are obtained.

▶ The Uses of Minerals (pages 124–125)

1. Any hard, colorful mineral that has a brilliant or glassy luster is called a(n)

   _____.

2. A gemstone that has been cut and polished is called a(n)

   _____.

3. Circle the letter of each choice that is a way gems are used.

    a. jewelry   **b.** fuel

    c. mechanical parts   **d.** grinding and polishing

4. List four examples of metals.

    a. _____   **b.** _____   **c.** _____   **d.** _____

5. Why are metals useful? _____

_____

_____

6. What are some uses of metals? _____

_____

_____

Match each mineral with the product in which it is found.

Mineral	Product
_____ **7.** talc	**a.** cement
_____ **8.** kaolin	**b.** microscopes
_____ **9.** calcite	**c.** watches
_____ **10.** quartz	**d.** powder
_____ **11.** gypsum	**e.** pottery

▶ **Ores** (page 125)

12. A rock that contains a metal or economically useful mineral is called

a(n) _____.

13. Is the following sentence true or false? Most metals occur in a pure

form. _____.

14. Much of the world's copper is contained in the mineral ore

_____.

CHAPTER 4, Minerals *(continued)*

▶ Prospecting (page 126)

15. Anyone who searches for an ore deposit is called a(n) _____.

16. What features do geologists look for when they prospect for ores?

_____

_____

_____

▶ Mining (pages 126–127)

17. Is the following sentence true or false? The map of an ore deposit helps

miners decide how to mine the ore. _____

18. Complete the compare/contrast table.

How Ores Are Mined	
Kind of Ore Deposit	**Type of Mine Used**
Starts near the surface and extends deep underground	
Occurs in veins	
Is exposed on the surface	

19. Describe strip mining. _____

_____

_____

20. Describe open pit mining. _____

_____

_____

21. Describe a shaft mine. _____

_____

_____

22. How can mining harm the environment? _____

_____

_____

_____

23. What do mine operators do to restore land damaged by strip mining?

_____

_____

▶ **Smelting** (pages 128–129)

24. The process in which an ore is melted to separate the useful metal from

other elements is _____.

25. Is the following sentence true or false? People first developed smelting

in the 1800s. _____

26. A solid mixture of two or more metals is called a(n) _____.

27. Fill in the flowchart with the following steps in the correct sequence:
produce carbon dioxide and molten iron, pour off molten iron, mix
with limestone and coal, place in blast furnace.

Smelting Iron Ore

```
┌─────────────────────────────────────┐
│                                     │
└─────────────────────────────────────┘
                  │
                  ▼
┌─────────────────────────────────────┐
│                                     │
└─────────────────────────────────────┘
                  │
                  ▼
┌─────────────────────────────────────┐
│                                     │
└─────────────────────────────────────┘
                  │
                  ▼
┌─────────────────────────────────────┐
│                                     │
└─────────────────────────────────────┘
```

CHAPTER 4, **Minerals** (continued)

WordWise

Use the clues to help you unscramble the key terms from Chapter 4. Then put the numbered letters in order to find the answer to the riddle.

Clues	Key Terms	
It's how it looks when it breaks.	tarfceur	_ _ _ _ _ _ _ _ 1
It contains two or more metals.	ylaol	_ _ _ _ _ 2
It could be shiny or pearly.	rutels	_ _ _ _ _ 3
It was never alive.	rincanoig	_ _ _ _ _ _ _ _ _ 4
It's the color of the powder.	rsaekt	_ _ _ _ _ _ 5
It includes melting.	temsilgn	_ _ _ _ _ _ _ _ 6
It has a repeating pattern.	ratlycs	_ _ _ _ _ _ _ 7
It contains two or more elements.	pucnoodm	_ _ _ _ _ _ _ _ 8
It's valued because it's beautiful and rare.	nsgoteem	_ _ _ _ _ _ _ 9
It's a mixture.	situnloo	_ _ _ _ _ _ _ _ 10
It's how it splits.	elagveac	_ _ _ _ _ _ _ _ 11
It's composed of a single kind of atom.	teemlen	_ _ _ _ _ _ _ 12

Riddle: Why do some minerals glow?

Answer: _ _ _ _ _ _ _ _ _ _ _ _
                1 2 3 4 5 6 7 8 9 10 11 12

CHAPTER 5

ROCKS

....

SECTION 5–1 ## Classifying Rocks
(pages 136–139)

This section explains how geologists classify rocks.

▶ How Geologists Classify Rocks (pages 136–137)

1. Earth's crust is made of _____.

2. What are rocks made of? _____

_____

_____

3. Circle the letter of each mineral that is found in granite.

   a. quartz   **b.** feldspar   **c.** mica   **d.** hornblende

4. Circle the letter of each characteristic that geologists use to classify rocks.

   a. texture   **b.** mineral composition

   c. hardness   **d.** color

▶ Texture (pages 137–138)

5. Is the following sentence true or false? Most rocks can be identified by

   color alone. _____

6. The look and feel of a rock's surface is its _____.

7. Particles of minerals and other rocks that make up a rock are called

   _____.

8. Is the following sentence true or false? A rock's grains give the rock its

   texture. _____

CHAPTER 5, Rocks *(continued)*

9. Circle the letter of each sentence that is true about the grain size in rock.

    a. An example of a coarse-grained rock is diorite.

    b. An example of a fine-grained rock is slate.

    c. Grains in fine-grained rock are easy to see.

    d. Grains in coarse-grained rock are microscopic.

10. Complete the concept map.

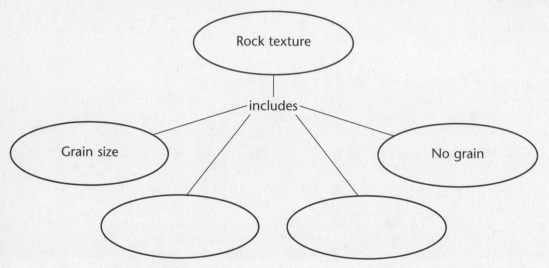

11. Circle the letter of the choice that determines the grain shape of a rock such as granite.

    a. Shape of the rock's crystals   **b.** Size of the rock's crystals

    c. Shape of fragments of other rock   **d.** Coarseness of the rock's grains

12. Circle the letter of the choice that determines the grain shape of a rock such as conglomerate.

    a. Shape of fragments of other rock   **b.** Size of the rock's grains

    c. Shape of the rock's crystals   **d.** Fineness of the rock's grains

13. Circle the letter of the description of the grain pattern of gneiss.

    a. It looks like rows of beads.

    b. It looks like a stack of pancakes.

    c. It looks like waves.

    d. It looks like rows of squares and rectangles.

14. Circle the letter of each sentence that is true about rocks with no visible grain.

    a. Some rocks have no visible grain even under a microscope.

    b. Some rocks without crystal grains cooled very quickly.

    c. Rocks without crystal grains look rough and coarse.

    d. An example of a rock with a glassy texture is slate.

▶ Mineral Composition (page 139)

15. How do geologists identify the minerals in a rock? _____

_____

_____

_____

16. To prepare a rock for viewing under the microscope, why must

geologists cut the rock very thin? _____

_____

17. Circle the letter of each element that could make a rock attract a magnet.

    a. sulphur   **b.** nitrogen   **c.** iron   **d.** nickel

▶ Origin (page 139)

18. List the three major groups of rock.

    a. _____ **b.** _____ **c.** _____

19. Complete the compare/contrast table.

How Rocks Form	
Type of Rock	**How It Forms**
	Molten rock cools.
	Particles are pressed and cemented.
	Existing rock is changed.

CHAPTER 5, Rocks *(continued)*

20. The type of rock that forms from magma or lava is _____ rock.

21. The type of rock that forms in layers is _____ rock.

22. Is the following sentence true or false? Most metamorphic rocks form

close to the surface. _____

· ·

SECTION 5–2 Igneous Rocks
(pages 140–143)

This section describes the characteristics and uses of igneous rocks.

▶ **Characteristics of Igneous Rock** (pages 141–142)

1. Circle the letter of the definition of igneous rock.

a. Rock that forms from minerals   **b.** Rock that contains iron

c. Rock that forms from magma or lava   **d.** Rock that contains crystals

2. Complete the Venn diagram by labeling each circle with the type of rock it represents.

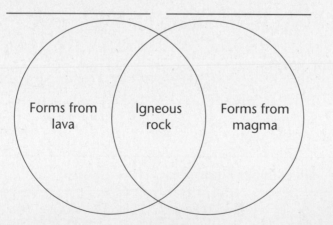

_____ _____

Forms from lava   Igneous rock   Forms from magma

3. Is the following sentence true or false? Extrusive rock forms beneath

Earth's surface. _____

4. Circle the letter of each sentence that is true about basalt.

a. It forms much of the crust.   **b.** It is the most common intrusive rock.

c. It forms from lava.   **d.** It forms beneath Earth's surface.

       Science Explorer *Focus on Earth Science*

5. Circle the letter of each sentence that is true about granite.

   a. It is the most abundant intrusive rock in continental crust.

   b. It forms the core of many mountain ranges.

   c. It forms from magma.

   d. It forms on top of the crust.

6. The texture of an igneous rock depends on the size and shape of its

   _____.

7. Is the following sentence true or false? Igneous rocks with similar

   mineral compositions always have the same textures. _____

Match the type of texture of igneous rocks with how rocks of that texture form.

Type of Texture	How Rocks of That Texture Form
_____ **8.** fine-grained	**a.** Magma cools in two stages.
_____ **9.** coarse-grained	**b.** Lava cools rapidly.
_____ **10.** porphyritic	**c.** Magma cools slowly.

11. Is the following sentence true or false? Intrusive rocks have smaller

   crystals than extrusive rocks. _____

12. A rock with large crystals scattered on a background of much smaller

   crystals has a(n) _____ texture.

13. What type of texture do extrusive rocks such as basalt have?

   _____

   _____

14. Circle the letter of each sentence that is true about the silica
   composition of igneous rocks.

   a. Igneous rocks low in silica are usually dark colored.

   b. An example of an igneous rock low in silica is granite.

   c. Igneous rocks high in silica are usually light colored.

   d. An example of an igneous rock high in silica is basalt.

CHAPTER 5, Rocks *(continued)*

▶ Uses of Igneous Rock (page 143)

15. Why have people throughout history used igneous rocks for tools and

building materials? _____

_____

_____

16. Complete the table.

How Some Igneous Rocks Are Used	
Type of Igneous Rock	**Way It Is Used**
Basalt	Gravel for construction
	Cleaning and polishing
	Soil mixes

📖 Reading Skill Practice

When you read about new or difficult concepts, making a concept map can help you better understand and remember the ideas. Make a concept map that shows how igneous rocks are classified, based on the material in Section 5-2. For more information on concept maps, see page 720 of the Skills Handbook in your text. Do your work on a separate sheet of paper.

· ·

SECTION 5–3 ## Sedimentary Rocks
(pages 144-148)

This section describes how sedimentary rocks form and how they are classified and used.

▶ From Sediment to Rock (pages 144–145)

1. Is the following sentence true or false? Sedimentary rocks form from

particles deposited by water and wind. _____

2. Small, solid pieces of material that come from rocks or living things are

called _____.

3. List three forces that can carry sediment.

a. _____ b. _____ c. _____

Match the process with its description.

Process

_____ **4.** erosion

_____ **5.** deposition

_____ **6.** compaction

_____ **7.** cementation

Description

a. Dissolved minerals glue sediments together.

b. Sediments are pressed together in layers.

c. Water or wind loosen and carry away fragments of rock.

d. Sediments settle out of water or wind.

8. What remains of living things may sediment include? _____

_____

_____

9. What happens to the remains of living things in sediment? _____

_____

_____

10. The process in which thick layers of sediment press down on the layers

beneath them is called _____.

11. Complete the flowchart to show how sediment is turned into
sedimentary rock.

Sedimentary Rock Formation

| Sediment | → | | → | | → | | → | Sedimentary rock |

12. Is the following sentence true or false? It takes millions of years for

sedimentary rock to form. _____

© Prentice-Hall, Inc.

CHAPTER 5, Rocks *(continued)*

▶ Types of Sedimentary Rock (page 146)

13. How do geologists classify sedimentary rock? _____

_____

_____

14. List the three major groups of sedimentary rock.

   a. _____ b. _____ c. _____

15. Is the following sentence true or false? The same process forms all types

   of sedimentary rock. _____

▶ Clastic Rocks (page 146)

16. Is the following sentence true or false? Clastic rocks form when rock

   fragments are squeezed together. _____

17. How are clastic rocks classified? _____

_____

_____

18. Complete the table.

How Clastic Rock Forms	
Type of Clastic Rock	**Material From Which It Forms**
	Tiny particles of clay
	Small particles of sand
	Different-sized rock fragments

▶ Organic Rocks (page 147)

19. The type of rocks that form where the remains of plants and animals

   are deposited in thick layers is called _____ rock.

20. List two important organic rocks.

a. _____   b. _____

21. Organic rock that forms from the remains of swamp plants buried in

water is _____.

22. How does organic limestone form? _____

_____

_____

_____

_____

23. What sediments form chalk? _____

_____

_____

▶ Chemical Rocks (page 148)

24. Circle the letter of each sentence that describes a way that chemical
rocks can form.

a. Minerals that are dissolved in a solution crystallize.

b. Sediments of plants and animals form oil and other chemicals in rock.

c. Mineral deposits form when seas or lakes evaporate.

d. Tiny particles of clay are cemented together with chemicals.

25. Is the following sentence true or false? Some limestone is considered to

be a chemical rock. _____

26. Rock salt crystallizes from the mineral _____.

27. Large deposits of rocks formed by evaporation form only in

_____ climates.

CHAPTER 5, Rocks *(continued)*

▶ Uses of Sedimentary Rocks (page 148)

28. Why have sandstone and limestone been used as building materials for

thousands of years? _____

_____

_____

29. Is the following sentence true or false? The White House in

Washington, D.C., is built of limestone. _____

30. What are some ways that builders today use sandstone and limestone?

_____

_____

_____

31. Is the following sentence true or false? Limestone is used for smelting

iron ore and making cement. _____

SECTION 5-4 **Rocks From Reefs** (pages 149-151)

This section explains how coral reefs form and how coral reefs can become limestone deposits.

▶ Living Coral (page 150)

1. Circle the letter of each sentence that is true about living coral.

    a. It is a tiny plant.   **b.** It is related to jellyfish.

    c. It lives in deep oceans.   **d.** It eats microscopic creatures.

2. Skeletons of living coral grow together to form a structure called a(n)

_____ .

3. Circle the letter of each sentence that is true about coral reefs.

a. They form only in cool water.

b. They form only in tropical oceans.

c. They form only in water low in salt.

d. They form only in deep water.

4. Where are coral reefs most abundant? _____

_____

_____

_____

5. In the United States, where are the only coral reefs found? _____

_____

_____

6. Is the following sentence true or false? Almost all growth in a coral reef

occurs close to the water's surface. _____

▶ How a Coral Reef Forms (pages 150–151)

7. Coral animals absorb the element _____ from ocean water.

8. The protective outer shells of coral animals are formed from

_____.

9. Circle the letter of each sentence that is true about the growth of coral reefs.

a. Coral reefs may grow to be hundreds of kilometers long.

b. Coral reefs may grow to be hundreds of kilometers thick.

c. Coral reefs usually grow inward away from the open ocean.

d. Coral reefs may grow for thousands of years.

10. The barrier reef that lies along the coast of Australia is named the

_____.

11. A ring-shaped coral island is called a(n) _____.

CHAPTER 5, Rocks (continued)

12. Where do atolls develop? _____

_____

_____

13. Complete the table.

Types of Coral Reefs and Where They Are Found	
Type of Reef	**Where It Is Found**
Fringing reef	
	At least 10 kilometers from land
	Far from land

▶ Limestone Deposits From Coral Reefs (page 151)

14. Where is limestone that began as coral found on continents?

_____

_____

15. Where in the United States are there exposed coral reefs? _____

_____

_____

© Prentice-Hall, Inc.

SECTION 5–5 Metamorphic Rocks (pages 152-154)

This section explains how metamorphic rocks form, how they are classified, and how they are used.

▶ How Metamorphic Rocks Form (page 152)

1. List the two forces that can change rocks into metamorphic rocks.

a. _____   b. _____

2. Is the following sentence true or false? Metamorphic rocks form deep

beneath Earth's surface. _____

3. How do rocks change when they become metamorphic rocks?

_____

_____

_____

4. What kinds of rocks can be changed into metamorphic rock?

_____

_____

_____

5. Is the following sentence true or false? The deeper a rock is buried in

the crust, the less pressure there is on that rock. _____

▶ **Classifying Metamorphic Rocks** (page 153)

6. Is the following sentence true or false? Geologists classify metamorphic
rocks by the arrangement of grains making up the rocks.

_____

7. Metamorphic rocks with grains arranged in parallel layers or bands are

said to be _____.

8. Circle the letter of each type of metamorphic rock that is foliated.
   a. slate   **b.** schist   **c.** gneiss   **d.** marble

9. Metamorphic rocks with grains arranged randomly are said to be

_____.

10. List two examples of nonfoliated metamorphic rocks.

   a. _____   **b.** _____

CHAPTER 5, Rocks *(continued)*

11. Complete the flowchart to show the metamorphic rocks that are formed.

How Some Metamorphic Rocks Form

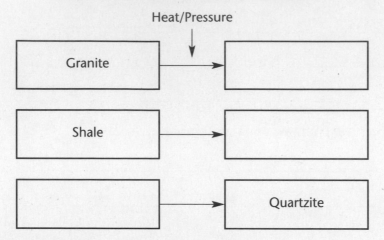

▶ Uses of Metamorphic Rock (page 154)

12. Why is marble useful for buildings and statues? _____

_____

_____

13. What are some of the ways that slate is used? _____

_____

_____

SECTION 5-6	**The Rock Cycle** (pages 156-159)

This section describes the cycle that builds, destroys, and changes rocks in Earth's crust. The section also explains how this cycle is related to movements in Earth's crust.

▶ A Cycle of Many Pathways (page 156)

1. The series of processes that slowly change rocks from one kind to

another is referred to as the _____.

2. What forces move rocks through the rock cycle? _____

_____

_____

3. Is the following sentence true or false? All rocks follow the same pathway

through the rock cycle. _____

▶ One Pathway Through the Rock Cycle (pages 157–158)

4. How could granite be changed into sandstone? _____

_____

_____

_____

5. Label the arrows in the cycle diagram, using the following terms:
erosion, melting, heat/pressure, volcanic activity. Some of the terms may
be used more than once.

The Rock Cycle

Igneous rock

Sedimentary rock

Magma

Metamorphic rock

▶ The Rock Cycle and Plate Tectonics (page 159)

6. How do plate movements drive the rock cycle? _____

_____

_____

_____

_____

CHAPTER 5, Rocks *(continued)*

WordWise

Test your knowledge of rocks by using key terms from Chapter 5 to solve the crossword puzzle.

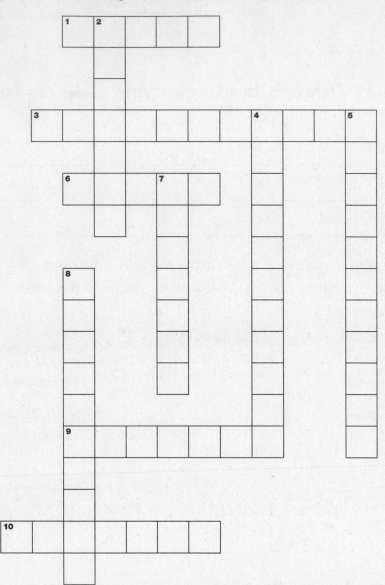

Clues across

1. Ring-shaped coral island
3. Rock formed by heat or pressure
6. Particle that gives rock texture
9. Sedimentary rock formed under pressure
10. Movement of fragments of rock

Clues down

2. Look and feel of a rock's surface
4. Igneous rock with big and small crystals
5. Process of gluing sediments
7. Rock formed from molten rock
8. Process of pressing sediments

CHAPTER 6

MAPPING EARTH'S SURFACE

. . . .

SECTION 6-1 **Exploring Earth's Surface**
(pages 172-176)

This section describes factors that determine the shape of Earth's land surface. The section also describes how scientists divide Earth into four spheres.

▶ **Topography** (pages 172–173)

1. The shape of the land is referred to as _____.

Match the term with its definition.

Term	Definition
_____ **2.** elevation	**a.** Difference in elevation
_____ **3.** relief	**b.** Height above sea level
_____ **4.** landform	**c.** Feature of topography

5. Write on the map where the following landform regions are found in the United States: coastal plains, interior plains, and mountains.

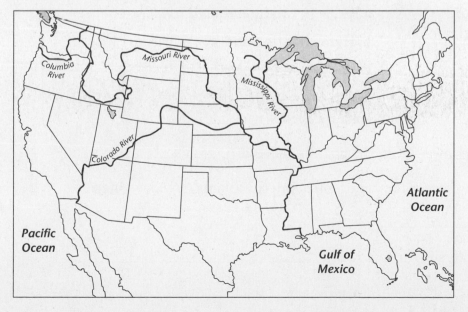

© Prentice-Hall, Inc.

CHAPTER 6, Mapping Earth's Surface (continued)

6. A large area of land where the topography is similar is called a(n)

_____.

7. List the five types of landform regions that are found in the United States.

a. _____   b. _____   c. _____

d. _____   e. _____

▶ Types of Landforms (pages 174–175)

8. Complete the concept map.

```
                    ┌─────────────┐
                   (  Major types  )
                   (  of landforms  )
                    └──────┬──────┘
                           │
                       include
               ┌───────────┼───────────┐
            (     )     (     )     (     )
             \___/       \___/       \___/
```

Match the type of landform with its characteristics.

Type of Landform	Characteristics
_____ **9.** plain	**a.** High elevation and high relief
_____ **10.** mountain	**b.** High elevation and level surface
_____ **11.** plateau	**c.** Flat land and low relief

12. A plain that lies along a seacoast is called a(n) _____.

13. A plain that lies away from the coast is called a(n) _____.

14. Is the following sentence true or false? Interior plains may have high

relief. _____

15. How is a plateau similar to a plain? _____

_____

16. Complete the table.

Mountain Landforms	
Type of Mountain Landform	**Description**
	Group of mountains
	Group of mountain ranges
	Group of mountain ranges and systems

▶ Earth's Four Spheres (page 176)

17. Earth's solid, rocky outer layer is called the _____.

18. Circle the letter of each sentence that is true about the atmosphere.

    a. It is Earth's inner sphere.

    b. Its water vapor condenses to form clouds.

    c. It contains several gases.

    d. Its most abundant gas is carbon dioxide.

19. Earth's oceans, lakes, rivers, and ice form the _____.

20. Is the following sentence true or false? Most of the hydrosphere consists of fresh water. _____

21. What makes up the biosphere? _____

_____

© Prentice-Hall, Inc.

SECTION 6-2 Models of Earth (pages 177-182)

This section describes how maps and globes are used as models of Earth. The section also explains how to locate points on Earth's surface using maps and globes.

▶ Maps and Globes (pages 177–178)

1. A model on a flat surface of all or part of Earth's surface is a(n)

_____.

CHAPTER 6, Mapping Earth's Surface *(continued)*

2. A sphere that represents Earth's entire surface as seen from space is a(n)

   _____.

Match the map feature with the role it plays.

Map Feature	Role It Plays
_____ 3. scale	**a.** Relates directions on a map to directions on Earth's surface
_____ 4. symbol	**b.** Stands for a feature on Earth's surface
_____ 5. key	**c.** Relates distance on a map to distance on Earth's surface
_____ 6. compass rose	**d.** Lists and explains all the symbols on a map

7. What are some of the physical and human-made features that map

   symbols can represent? _____

   _____

   _____

8. What does a map scale of 1:25,000 mean? _____

   _____

   _____

▶ An Earth Reference System (pages 179–180)

9. The imaginary line that circles Earth halfway between the North and

   South poles is the _____.

10. Half of Earth's surface is called a(n) _____.

11. Circle the letter of each sentence that is true about the prime meridian.

    a. It circles the globe from the North Pole to the South Pole.

    b. It passes through Washington, D.C.

    c. It divides Earth into the Northern and Southern hemispheres.

    d. It passes through the Northern and Southern hemispheres

© Prentice-Hall, Inc.

12. The units scientists use to measure distances around a circle are

_____.

▶ Locating Points on Earth's Surface (pages 180–181)

13. Circle the letter of each sentence that is true about latitude.

   a. The prime meridian is the starting line for measuring latitude.

   b. Latitude measures distance in degrees north or south of the equator.

   c. All lines of latitude are parallel to the equator.

   d. The latitude of the North Pole is 90° north.

14. Circle the letter of each sentence that is true about longitude.

   a. The equator is the starting line for measuring longitude.

   b. Longitude measures distance in degrees east or west of the prime meridian.

   c. All lines of longitude meet at the equator.

   d. Lines of longitude cross lines of latitude at right angles.

15. Label the lines on the map with the following terms: equator, prime meridian, 30°N latitude, 30°W longitude.

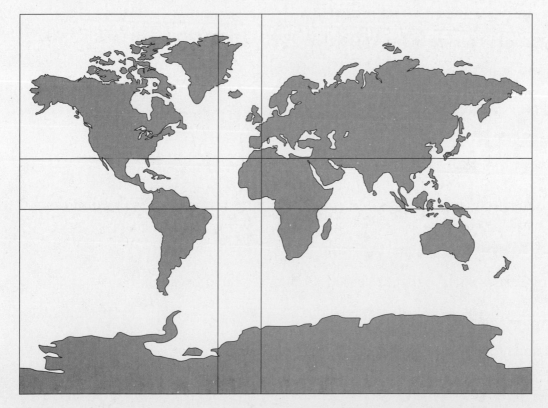

CHAPTER 6, Mapping Earth's Surface *(continued)*

16. What is the longitude of the prime meridian? _____

_____

▶ Map Projections (page 182)

17. What is a map projection? _____

_____

_____

18. Circle the letter of each sentence that is true about a Mercator projection.

   a. Lines of longitude meet at the poles.

   b. Landmasses near the poles are distorted.

   c. Sizes of landmasses are changed.

   d. Greenland appears too small.

19. Circle the letter of each sentence that is true about an equal-area projection.

   a. Lines of longitude are parallel.

   b. Landmasses near the edges are distorted.

   c. Sizes of landmasses are shown correctly.

   d. Greenland appears too large.

· ·

SECTION 6-3 Maps in the Computer Age (pages 184-186)

This section describes how satellites and computers have revolutionized mapmaking.

▶ Satellite Mapping (pages 184–185)

1. Pictures of Earth's surface that are based on data collected by satellites

are called _____.

2. What is Landsat? _____

_____

▶ Computer Mapping (page 186)

3. How do mapmakers use computers? _____

_____

_____

4. The process by which mapmakers convert the location of map points to

numbers for use in computer mapping is called _____.

 **Reading Skill Practice**

When you read about complex processes, writing an outline can help you organize and understand the material. Outline Section 6-3 by using the headings and subheadings as topics and subtopics of your outline and then writing the most important details under each topic. Do your work on a separate sheet of paper.

SECTION 6-4 Topographic Maps (pages 187-191)

This section describes a special type of map, called a topographic map. It also describes how and why topographic maps are used. In addition, the section describes a network of satellites that is used to determine precisely locations on Earth's surface.

▶ Mapping Earth's Topography (pages 187–188)

1. A map that shows the surface features of an area is called a(n)

_____ map.

2. List three types of information about the ground surface that are provided by topographic maps.

a. _____ b. _____ c. _____

CHAPTER 6, Mapping Earth's Surface *(continued)*

3. Why might you use a topographic map if you were planning a bicycle

    trip? _____

    _____

    _____

4. What is a large-scale map? _____

    _____

    _____

▶ Showing Relief on Topographic Maps (pages 189–190)

5. List the three features that contour lines show on a topographic map.

    a. _____ b. _____ c. _____

6. The change in elevation from contour line to contour line is called the

    _____.

7. Is the following sentence true or false? The contour interval for a given

    topographic map is always the same. _____

8. Label each section of topographic map to indicate whether it shows a
   steep slope, a gentle slope, a depression, or a hilltop.

    _____   _____   _____   _____

9. Is the following sentence true or false? Every other contour line on a

    topographic map is labeled with the elevation. _____

10. How close the contour lines are is an indication of an area's

     _____.

11. Circle the letter that gives the meaning of the index number on a contour line.

    a. Elevation above sea level   **b.** Longitude and latitude

    c. Distance from the equator   **d.** Distance from the North Pole

12. What do V-shaped contour lines pointing downhill indicate?

_____

13. Circle the number of contour lines you would need to show a change in elevation of 1,000 feet on a map with a contour interval of 200 feet.

    a. 5   **b.** 10   **c.** 20   **d.** 50

14. Circle the contour interval if ten contour lines show a change in elevation of 2,000 feet.

    a. 10 feet   **b.** 100 feet   **c.** 200 feet   **d.** 500 feet

▶ Global Positioning System (page 191)

15. What is the Global Positioning System? _____

_____

_____

_____

16. How can engineers use the Global Positioning System? _____

_____

_____

_____

17. How can drivers use the Global Positioning System? _____

_____

_____

_____

_____

CHAPTER 6, Mapping Earth's Surface (continued)

WordWise

Solve the clues to determine which key terms from Chapter 6 are hidden in the puzzle. Then find and circle the terms in the puzzle. The terms may occur vertically, horizontally, or diagonally.

Clues	Hidden Words
Unit that measures distances around a circle	_____
Feature of topography formed by processes that shape Earth's surface	_____
List of the symbols used on a map	_____
Model of all or part of Earth's surface as seen from above	_____
Landform of flat or gently rolling land with low relief	_____
Half of the sphere that makes up Earth's surface	_____
Distance in degrees north or south of the equator	_____
Imaginary line that circles Earth halfway between the poles	_____
Picture used by mapmakers to stand for a feature on Earth's surface	_____
Difference in elevation between the highest and lowest parts of an area	_____
Mixture of gases that surrounds Earth	_____
Earth's water and ice	_____
All living things on Earth	_____
Distance in degrees east or west of the prime meridian	_____
Landform with high elevation and high relief	_____

```
p  l  b  r  c  d  e  g  m  o  z
l  a  d  e  g  r  e  e  a  x  m
a  t  s  l  a  n  d  f  o  r  m
i  i  p  i  t  g  h  t  t  l  m
n  t  a  e  m  j  y  l  n  o  o
h  u  n  f  o  f  d  q  u  n  u
e  d  r  w  s  t  r  b  r  g  n
m  e  e  v  p  c  o  i  f  i  t
i  e  p  c  h  i  s  o  p  t  a
s  q  s  d  e  k  p  s  o  u  i
p  u  y  a  r  p  h  p  a  d  n
h  a  m  m  e  y  e  h  t  e  m
e  t  b  r  e  p  r  e  i  r  d
r  o  o  k  a  e  e  r  c  u  w
e  r  l  m  k  m  e  e  h  q  g
```

Science Explorer *Focus on Earth Science*

CHAPTER 7

WEATHERING AND SOIL FORMATION

. . . .

SECTION 7-1 **Rocks and Weathering**
(pages 198-203)

This section describes how rocks are broken down by forces of weathering. The section also describes factors that determine how quickly weathering occurs.

▶ **The Effects of Weathering** (pages 198–199)

Match the process with its description.

Process

_____ 1. weathering

_____ 2. erosion

Description

a. Movement of rock particles by wind, water, ice, or gravity

b. Breaking down of rock and other substances at Earth's surface

3. Complete the concept map.

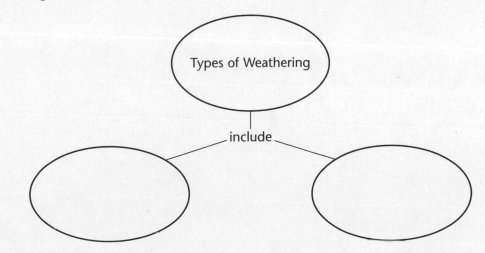

▶ **Mechanical Weathering** (pages 199–200)

4. The type of weathering in which rock is physically broken into smaller

pieces is called _____ weathering.

CHAPTER 7, Weathering and Soil Formation (continued)

5. List the forces of mechanical weathering.

a. _____   b. _____   c. _____

d. _____   e. _____

6. What is abrasion? _____

_____

_____

7. Complete the cycle diagram.

Ice Wedging

Water seeps into cracks.

Ice widens cracks.

▶ Chemical Weathering (pages 201–202)

8. The process that breaks down rock through chemical changes is

_____ weathering.

9. List the agents of chemical weathering.

a. _____   b. _____   c. _____

d. _____   e. _____

10. Is the following sentence true or false? Chemical weathering produces rock particles with the same mineral makeup as the rock they came

from. _____

Match the agent of chemical weathering with the statement that is true about it.

Agent of Chemical Weathering	Statement

_____ 11. water

_____ 12. oxygen

_____ 13. carbon dioxide

_____ 14. living organisms

_____ 15. acid rain

a. It causes iron to rust.

b. It's caused by pollution.

c. It's the most important agent.

d. It forms carbonic acid.

e. Lichens are one example.

16. Is the following sentence true or false? Water weathers rock by

gradually dissolving it. _____

17. Oxygen weathers rock through a process called _____.

18. List two kinds of rock that are easily weathered by carbonic acid.

a. _____   b. _____

19. How do plants dissolve rock? _____

_____

_____

▶ Rate of Weathering (page 203)

20. The most important factors that determine the rate of weathering are

type of rock and _____.

21. Is the following sentence true or false? The minerals that make up a

rock determine how fast it weathers. _____

22. A rock that is full of tiny, connected air spaces is said to be

_____.

23. Why does a permeable rock weather chemically at a fast rate? _____

_____

_____

CHAPTER 7, Weathering and Soil Formation *(continued)*

24. Why does chemical weathering occur more quickly in a hot climate?

_____

_____

_____

· ·

SECTION 7-2 **Soil Formation and Composition**
(pages 207-213)

This section explains how soil forms. The section also describes several features of soil, the living things found in soil, and the types of soil found in the United States.

▶ **Soil Formation** (page 207)

1. The loose, weathered material on Earth's surface in which plants can

   grow is _____.

2. How does soil form? _____

   _____

   _____

3. The solid layer of rock beneath the soil is called _____.

▶ **Soil Composition** (page 208)

4. What two factors determine the type of rock particles and minerals in

   any given soil? _____

   _____

   _____

5. List the three types of weathered rock particles found in soil.

   a. _____ b. _____ c. _____

6. The decayed organic material in soil is called _____.

▶ Soil Texture (page 208)

7. Circle the letter of the choice that lists soil particles from largest to smallest.

    a. sand, gravel, clay, silt

    b. gravel, sand, silt, clay

    c. gravel, silt, sand, clay

    d. gravel, sand, clay, silt

8. Soil that is made up of about equal parts of clay, sand, and silt is called

    _____.

▶ Soil Horizons (page 209)

Match the soil horizon with its makeup.

Soil Horizon	Makeup
_____ **9.** A	**a.** Topsoil
_____ **10.** B	**b.** Rock particles
_____ **11.** C	**c.** Subsoil

12. Label each of the soil horizons shown in the three drawings as A, B, or C horizon.

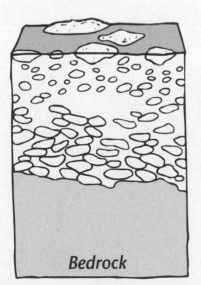

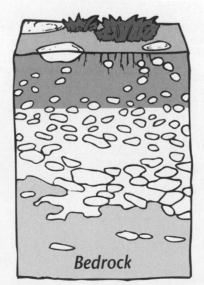

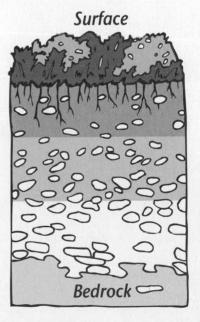

CHAPTER 7, Weathering and Soil Formation *(continued)*

▶ Rate of Soil Formation (page 209)

13. Circle the letter of each sentence that is true about the rate of soil formation.

 a. It is faster in areas that are cold.

 b. It is slower in areas that are dry.

 c. It is faster with limestone than granite.

 d. It is unaffected by the type of rock being weathered.

▶ Life in Soil (pages 210–212)

14. How do soil organisms improve soil? _____

_____

_____

15. Is the following sentence true or false? Animals contribute most of the

organic remains that form humus. _____

16. As plants shed leaves, they form a loose layer called _____.

17. Soil organisms that turn dead organic matter into humus are called

_____.

18. List the main soil decomposers.

 a. _____ **b.** _____ **c.** _____ **d.** _____

19. Circle the letter of each choice that is an example of fungi.

 a. molds **b.** mushrooms **c.** bacteria **d.** earthworms

20. Is the following sentence true or false? Earthworms do most of the

work of mixing humus with other materials in soil. _____

21. How can burrowing mammals improve soil? _____

_____

_____

▶ Soil Types in the United States (pages 212–213)

22. Circle the letter of each factor that scientists use to classify the different types of soil into groups.

    a. climate

    b. plant types

    c. soil composition

    d. size of animal populations

23. Is the following sentence true or false? The soil type of northeastern

United States and Canada is southern forest soils. _____

Reading Skill Practice

When you read a section that contains new or difficult material, identifying the sentence that best expresses the main topic under each heading can help you focus on the most important points. For each heading in Section 7–2, identify and copy the sentence that best expresses the main topic under that heading. Do your work on a separate sheet of paper.

SECTION 7-3 Soil Conservation (pages 215-218)

This section explains why soil is valuable. The section also explains how soil can be damaged or lost, as well as how it can be conserved.

▶ Introduction (page 215)

1. The thick mass of tough roots at the surface of the soil is called

_____.

2. Is the following sentence true or false? Prairie soils are no longer among

the most fertile soils in the world. _____

CHAPTER 7, Weathering and Soil Formation (continued)

▶ The Value of Soil (pages 215–216)

3. Why is soil one of Earth's most valuable resources? _____

_____

_____

4. Is the following sentence true or false? Soil can be found wherevcr

weathering occurs. _____

5. Circle the letter of each sentence that is true about soil.

   a. Soil is a nonrenewable resource.

   b. Soil formation takes a long time.

   c. Fertile soil is plentiful.

   d. Half of Earth has soils good for farming

▶ Soil Damage and Loss (page 216)

6. How can soil be damaged? _____

_____

7. How can soil be lost? _____

_____

8. How can plants protect soil from water erosion? _____

_____

_____

▶ The Dust Bowl (page 217)

9. Circle the letter of each sentence that is true about the Great Plains.

   a. The Great Plains are farther west than the prairies.

   b. The Great Plains are drier than the prairies.

   c. The Great Plains begin at the Appalachian Mountains.

   d. The Great Plains have never been farmed or used for ranches.

10. Circle the letter of each state that was part of the Dust Bowl.

    a. Oklahoma   **b.** Kansas   **c.** Texas   **d.** Missouri

11. Why did the Dust Bowl occur? _____

_____

_____

_____

▶ Soil Conservation (page 218)

12. The management of soil to prevent its destruction is referred to as

    _____.

13. Why did the Dust Bowl lead to the adoption of modern methods of soil

    conservation? _____

_____

_____

14. Complete the Venn diagram.

_____ _____

Involves plowing along curves

Conserves soil

Disturbs soil as little as possible

15. How can livestock damage soil? _____

_____

_____

CHAPTER 7, Weathering and Soil Formation (continued)

WordWise

Test your knowledge of key terms from Chapter 7 by solving the clues. Then copy the numbered letters in order to reveal the hidden message.

Clues   **Key Terms**

Process of moving fragments of rock and soil

__ __ __ __ __ __ __
  1   2

Solid layer of rock beneath soil

__ __ __ __ __ __ __
         3 4

Thick mass of grass roots and soil

__ __ __
 5

Grinding away of rock by rock particles

__ __ __ __ __ __ __
  6

Loose layer of dead plant material on the soil surface

__ __ __ __ __ __
        7

Organisms that break down wastes and dead organisms

__ __ __ __ __ __ __ __ __ __ __
        8   9

Organic material in soil

__ __ __ __ __
   10

Processes that break down rock at Earth's surface

__ __ __ __ __ __ __ __ __ __
  11

Topmost layer of soil

__ __ __ __ __ __ __
      12

Soil with about equal parts of clay, sand, and silt

__ __ __ __
  13

Layer of soil beneath the topsoil

__ __ __ __ __ __ __
      14

Loose, weathered material in which plants can grow

__ __ __ __
   15

Hidden Message

__ __ __ __ __   __ __ __ __ __ __   __ __ __ __ .
1 2 3 4 5   6 7 8 9 10 11   12 13 14 15

CHAPTER 8

EROSION AND DEPOSITION

....

SECTION 8-1 Changing Earth's Surface (pages 224-227)

This section explains how sediment is carried away and deposited elsewhere to wear down and build up Earth's surface. The section also describes ways that gravity moves sediment downhill.

▶ Wearing Down and Building Up (page 225)

1. What is erosion? _____
_____
_____

2. List the forces that cause erosion.

   a. _____ b. _____ c. _____

   d. _____ e. _____

3. The material moved by erosion is called _____.

4. Where does deposition occur? _____
_____
_____

▶ Mass Movement (pages 225–227)

5. Circle the letter of each sentence that is true about gravity.

   a. It pulls things toward Earth's center.

   b. It causes landslides.

   c. It causes mass movement.

   d. It is a force of erosion.

CHAPTER 8, Erosion and Deposition *(continued)*

6. Is the following sentence true or false? The most destructive kind of

   mass movement is creep. _____

7. Is the following sentence true or false? Mudflows and slump are

   especially likely in soils high in clay. _____

8. Complete the concept map.

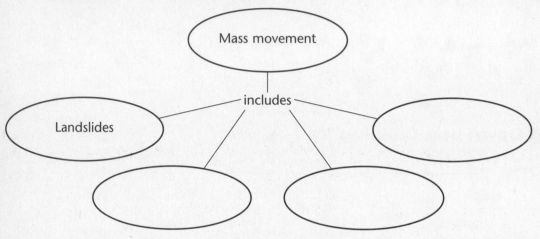

Match the type of mass movement with its description.

Type of Mass Movement   **Description**

_____ **9.** landslide   **a.** Rock and soil suddenly slip down a slope
                                       in one large mass.

_____ **10.** mudflow   **b.** Rock and soil slide quickly down a slope.

_____ **11.** slump   **c.** Rock and soil move very slowly downhill.

_____ **12.** creep   **d.** A mixture of water, rock, and soil moves
                                       rapidly downhill.

© Prentice-Hall, Inc.

📖 Reading Skill Practice

When reading about cyclical processes, making a cycle diagram can help you understand how the processes are related. As you read or review Section 8-1, make a cycle diagram showing how the processes of weathering, erosion, and deposition are related. For more information on cycle diagrams, see page 721 in the Skills Handbook of the textbook. Do your work on a separate sheet of paper.

SECTION 8-2 Water Erosion (pages 230–239)

This section describes how moving water erodes and deposits sediment to create landforms such as valleys and deltas.

▶ Runoff and Erosion (pages 231–232)

1. Is the following sentence true or false? Moving water is the major agent

   of erosion. _____

2. Water that moves over Earth's surface when it rains is called

   _____.

3. Fill in the first column of the table with the correct form of moving water.

Forms of Moving Water	
Form	**Description**
	Tiny groove in soil formed by runoff
	Channel that carries runoff after a rainstorm
	Channel with water continually flowing down a slope
	Large stream

4. Other than how people use the land, list four factors that determine the amount of runoff in an area.

   a. _____   b. _____

   c. _____   d. _____

5. Is the following sentence true or false? More runoff generally means less

   erosion. _____

▶ River Systems (pages 232–233)

6. A stream that flows into a larger stream is called a(n) _____.

CHAPTER 8, Erosion and Deposition *(continued)*

7. The area of land from which a river and its tributaries collect water is

   the _____.

8. Is the following sentence true or false? The high ground between two

   drainage basins is called a divide. _____

▶ Erosion by Rivers (pages 233–234)

9. How do V-shaped valleys form? _____

   _____

   _____

10. When does a river develop meanders? _____

    _____

11. A meander that has been cut off from a river is called a(n)

    _____.

12. Identify and label each of the following landforms in the illustration:
    waterfall, oxbow lake, meander, flood plain, and V-shaped valley.

▶ Deposits by Rivers (pages 235–237)

13. List two landforms created from deposits by rivers.

a. _____   b. _____

14. What is an alluvial fan? _____

_____

_____

15. Sediments deposited where a river flows into an ocean or lake form

a(n) _____.

16. What makes a river valley fertile? _____

_____

▶ Groundwater Erosion and Deposition (pages 238–239)

17. Underground water is called _____.

18. Is the following sentence true or false? Unlike moving surface water,

groundwater does not cause erosion. _____

19. How does groundwater cause chemical weathering of limestone?

_____

_____

20. Complete the compare/contrast table.

Groundwater Deposits In Limestone Caves	
Type of Deposit	**Where It Forms**
	Roof of cave
	Floor of cave

21. Is the following sentence true or false? An area where sinkholes are

common is said to have karst topography. _____

CHAPTER 8, Erosion and Deposition *(continued)*

The Force of Moving Water
(pages 243-246)

This section explains why moving water has energy and how it erodes and carries sediment. The section also identifies the factors that determine how much sediment a river can erode and carry.

▶ Work and Energy (pages 243–244)

1. The ability to do work or cause change is _____.

2. Energy that is stored for later use is called _____ energy.

3. Is the following statement true or false? Kinetic energy is the energy an

   object has due to its motion. _____

▶ How Water Erodes and Carries Sediment (page 244)

4. In what ways can sediment enter a river? _____

   _____

   _____

   _____

5. The wearing away of rock by a grinding action is called

   _____.

6. Is the following sentence true or false? Sediment in a river abrades the

   streambed and is abraded by the streambed in return. _____

7. The amount of sediment that a river carries is its _____.

8. Circle the letter of each sentence that is true about a river's sediment.

   a. Gravity and the force of the water cause sediment to move downstream.

   b. Most small sediments move by rolling and sliding along the bottom.

   c. Most large sediments move by bouncing.

   d. Some sediments are dissolved by the water and carried in solution.

▶ Erosion and Sediment Load (pages 245–246)

9. Complete the concept map.

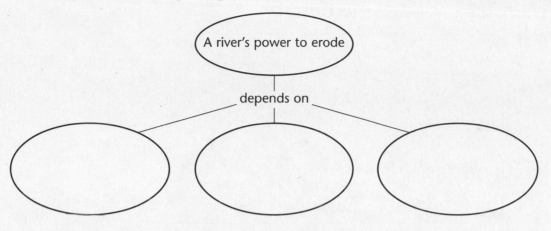

10. Is the following sentence true or false? When a river slows down and deposits its sediment load, smaller particles of sediment are deposited first. _____

11. Circle the letter of each factor that increases the speed of a river.

    a. Steep slope   **b.** Low volume

    c. Deep streambed   **d.** Boulders in streambed

12. Circle the letter of each factor that decreases the speed of a river.

    a. Gentle slope   **b.** High volume

    c. Shallow streambed   **d.** Boulders in streambed

Match the term with its definition.

Term	Definition
_____ **13.** flow	**a.** Movement of water every which way instead of downstream
_____ **14.** friction	**b.** Force that opposes the motion of one surface across another
_____ **15.** turbulence	**c.** Volume of water that moves past a point on a river in a given time

16. Is the following sentence true or false? Where a river flows in a straight line, the water flows faster along the river's sides than near the center.

_____

CHAPTER 8, Erosion and Deposition *(continued)*

17. Label the drawing to show where the river erodes sediment and where it deposits sediment as it flows around the curve.

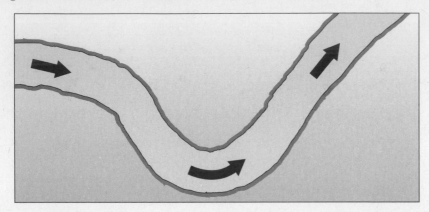

. . . .

SECTION 8-4 **Glaciers** (pages 247-251)

This section describes huge ice masses, called glaciers. The section also describes the ice ages, a time when glaciers covered much of Earth. In addition, the section explains how glaciers form and move and how they cause erosion and deposition.

▶ Kinds of Glaciers (pages 247-248)

1. Any large mass of ice that moves slowly over land is a(n)

 _____.

2. Circle the letter of each sentence that is true about valley glaciers.

    a. They are long, narrow glaciers.

    b. They are found on many high mountains.

    c. They are larger than continental glaciers.

    d. They follow river valleys.

3. Circle the letter of each sentence that is true about continental glaciers.

    a. They are larger than valley glaciers.

    b. They spread out over wide areas.

    c. They are found only in Antarctica.

    d. They cover 2 percent of Earth.

▶ Ice Ages (page 248)

4. What are ice ages? _____

_____

_____

5. Is the following sentence true or false? The most recent ice age ended

about 10,000 years ago. _____

6. Is the following sentence true or false? All of North America was covered

by a continental glacier in the last ice age. _____

▶ How Glaciers Form and Move (page 248)

7. Where can glaciers form? _____

_____

8. When does gravity begin to pull a glacier downhill? _____

_____

_____

9. Complete the table.

How Glaciers Move	
Type of Glacier	**How It Moves**
	Flows in all directions
	Flows in a surge

▶ Glacial Erosion (pages 248–249)

10. List two processes by which glaciers erode the land.

a. _____   b. _____

11. Is the following sentence true or false? Plucking can move only small

stones. _____

CHAPTER 8, Erosion and Deposition *(continued)*

12. Describe the process of abrasion by a glacier and the effect abrasion has

on the bedrock. _____

_____

_____

▶ Glacial Deposition (pages 249–251)

13. When does a glacier deposit the sediment it is carrying? _____

_____

_____

Match each type of glacial landform with its description.

Type of Landform	Description
_____ **14.** till	**a.** Small depression formed by a chunk of ice and filled with water
_____ **15.** moraine	**b.** Mixture of sediments a glacier deposits on the surface
_____ **16.** terminal moraine	**c.** Ridge formed at the edge of a glacier
_____ **17.** prairie pothole	**d.** Shallow depression formed by flowing water
_____ **18.** kettle	**e.** Ridge at the farthest point reached by a glacier
_____ **19.** cirque	**f.** Sharp ridge separating two cirques
_____ **20.** arête	**g.** Bowl-shape hollow eroded by a glacier
_____ **21.** fiord	**h.** Sea-filled valley cut by a glacier in a coastal region

22. How were the Great Lakes formed? _____

_____

_____

_____

SECTION 8-5 Waves (pages 252-255)

This section explains how waves form. The section also describes the erosion and deposition that waves cause.

▶ How Waves Form (pages 252-253)

1. Circle the letter of each sentence that is true about the energy in waves.

   a. It comes from wind.

   b. It moves water particles up and down.

   c. It moves water particles forward.

   d. It moves across the water.

2. What part of the water is affected by a wave in deep water? _____

   _____

   _____

3. Circle the letter of each sentence that is true about a wave approaching land.

   a. It begins to drag on the bottom.

   b. It encounters more friction.

   c. It speeds up.

   d. It moves the water toward the land.

▶ Erosion by Waves (page 253)

4. Is the following sentence true or false? Waves are the major force of

   erosion along coasts. _____

5. List two ways that waves erode land.

   a. _____   **b.** _____

6. Part of the shore that sticks out into the ocean because it is made of

   harder rock is called a(n) _____ .

CHAPTER 8, Erosion and Deposition *(continued)*

▶ Landforms Created by Wave Erosion (page 254)

7. List three landforms created by wave erosion.

   a. _____ b. _____ c. _____

▶ Deposits by Waves (pages 254–255)

8. An area of wave-washed sediment along a coast is a(n)

   _____.

9. The process in which beach sediment is moved down the beach with

   the current is called _____.

10. How does a spit form? _____

    _____

    _____

....

SECTION 8-6 Wind (pages 256-258)

This section describes how wind causes erosion. The section also describes the types of deposits that are caused by wind.

▶ Introduction (page 256)

1. A deposit of wind-blown sand is a(n) _____.

▶ How Wind Causes Erosion (pages 256–257)

2. Is the following sentence true or false? Wind alone is the strongest

   agent of erosion. _____

3. Why is wind very effective at causing erosion in deserts? _____

   _____

   _____

4. Circle the letter of each sentence that is true about deflation.

    a. It is the main way wind causes erosion.

    b. It usually has a great effect on the land.

    c. It can create blowouts.

    d. It can create desert pavement.

5. Circle the letter of each sentence that is true about abrasion.

    a. It can polish rock.

    b. It is caused by wind-carried sand.

    c. It causes most desert landforms.

    d. It causes most erosion.

▶ Deposits Resulting From Wind Erosion (page 258)

6. Is the following sentence true or false? All the sediment picked up by

wind eventually falls to the ground. _____

7. When does wind-carried sediment fall to the ground? _____

_____

_____

8. List two types of deposits formed by wind erosion and deposition.

    a. _____   **b.** _____

9. Complete the Venn diagram by adding the following phrases: have finer
sediments, have coarser sediments, result from wind erosion.

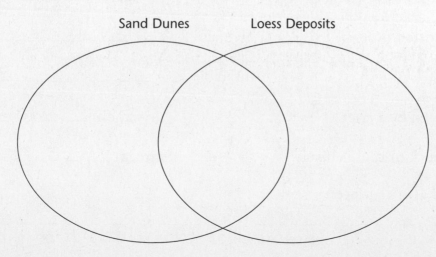

Sand Dunes   Loess Deposits

CHAPTER 8, Erosion and Deposition (continued)

WordWise

Use the clues to help you unscramble the key terms from Chapter 8. Then put the numbered letters in the right order to spell out the answer to the riddle.

Clues   **Key Terms**

It's how sediment moves.   sorineo _ _ _ _ _ _ _
                                                                                    1 2

It's how sediment settles.   oisontipde _ _ _ _ _ _ _ _ _ _
                                                                                         3

It's a small particle that moves.   ideemtns _ _ _ _ _ _ _ _
                                                                                    4   5

It's how much sediment a river carries.   adol _ _ _ _
                                                                                    6

It's the force that opposes motion   nfcotiri _ _ _ _ _ _ _ _
of one surface across another.   7

It's how rocks are polished.   barinoas _ _ _ _ _ _ _ _
                                                                                    8   9

It can be found where a river enters a lake.   ldtae _ _ _ _ _
                                                                                    10

It separates two drainage basins.   vdeiid _ _ _ _ _ _
                                                                                 11

It's formed by a chunk of ice.   teketl _ _ _ _ _ _
                                                                                    12

It sticks out in the water like a finger.   ipst _ _ _ _
                                                                                    13

It's a ridge at the edge of a glacier.   noamire _ _ _ _ _ _ _
                                                                                    14

It's a deposit of clay and silt.   seols _ _ _ _ _
                                                                                          15

It's how most wind erosion occurs.   otefdalni _ _ _ _ _ _ _ _ _
                                                                                          16

It flows into a larger stream.   tutyrabir _ _ _ _ _ _ _ _ _
                                                                                 17   18

It's a kind of lake created by a river.   wxoob _ _ _ _ _
                                                                                    19

It's the ability to do work or cause change.   ynreeg _ _ _ _ _ _
                                                                                    20

Riddle: What shapes Earth's surface?

Answer: _ _ _ _ _ _ _   _ _ _   _ _ _ _ _ _ _ _ _ _
                   1 2 3 4 5 6 7   8 9 10   11 12 13 14 15 16 17 18 19 20

CHAPTER 9

Earth: The Water Planet

• •

SECTION 9–1 How Is Water Important?
(pages 268-274)

This section describes ways that people use water and explains why living things need water. The section also describes how water is distributed on Earth.

▶ How Do People Use Water? (pages 268–270)

1. What are the ways that people use water? _____

_____

_____

_____

2. Is the following sentence true or false? All parts of the United States

receive enough regular rainfall for agriculture. _____

3. The process of supplying water to areas of land to make them suitable

for growing crops is called _____.

4. Is the following sentence true or false? In the United States, more water

is used for industry than for any other single purpose. _____

5. How is water used in the paper-making process? _____

_____

_____

6. What is another way water is used in industry? _____

_____

_____

CHAPTER 9, Earth: The Water Planet *(continued)*

7. Is the following sentence true or false? Oceans and rivers have been used for transporting people and goods since ancient times.

   _____

8. What led to the growth of port cities such as Boston, New York, and

   San Francisco? _____

9. Name several ways that water is used for recreation. _____

   _____

▶ Water and Living Things (pages 271–272)

10. Is the following sentence true or false? Water makes up one third of the

    human body. _____

11. The place where an organism lives and that provides the things it needs

    to survive is its _____.

12. Is the following sentence true or false? Neither fresh water nor salt

    water provide habitats for many living things. _____

▶ Water on Earth (pages 272–274)

13. Why is Earth called the "water planet"? _____

    _____

14. Label the circle graph to show the percentage of Earth's water that is
    salt water and the percentage that is fresh water.

Distribution of Water on Earth

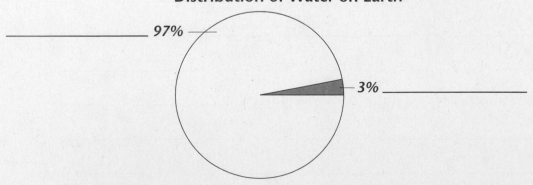

_____ 97%

3% _____

15. The gaseous form of water is called _____.

16. Circle the letter of each sentence that is true about fresh water on Earth.

    a. About three quarters of Earth's fresh water is in ice masses near the poles.

    b. Most fresh water in the atmosphere is in the form of water vapor.

    c. Less than 1 percent of all the water on earth is fresh water that humans can use.

    d. Some of Earth's fresh water is deep underground.

17. Circle the letter of each sentence that is true about the oceans on Earth.

    a. All Earth's oceans are connected to form a single world ocean.

    b. The Atlantic Ocean is deeper than the Indian Ocean.

    c. The Pacific Ocean covers more area than all Earth's land put together.

    d. The Arctic Ocean is next to the Indian Ocean.

18. Is the following sentence true or false? Icebergs are formed from frozen

salt water. _____

19. Water that fills the cracks and spaces in underground soil and rock

laycrs is called _____.

- -

SECTION 9–2 **The Properties of Water**
(pages 275–281)

This section describes water's properties. The section also describes the way water changes state, or form.

▶ Water's Unique Structure (pages 275–276)

  1. Circle the letter of each sentence that is true about water's structure.

    a. Water is made up of atoms bonded to form molecules.

    b. Water contains half as many hydrogen atoms as oxygen atoms.

    c. Water molecules tend to push away from each other.

    d. The chemical formula for water is H_2O.

CHAPTER 9, Earth: The Water Planet *(continued)*

2. A molecule that has electrically charged areas is called a(n)

_____ molecule.

▶ **Surface Tension** (page 276)

3. Circle the letter of each sentence that is true about water's surface tension.

   a. It helps insects "skate" across the surface of the water.

   b. It refers to the tightness across the surface of the water.

   c. It is caused by polar molecules repelling each other.

   d. It causes raindrops to form round beads.

4. How does surface tension force the surface of water to curve? _____

_____

_____

▶ **Capillary Action** (page 277)

5. Circle the letter of each sentence that is true about capillary action.

   a. It explains how water moves against the force of gravity.

   b. It is due to the attraction among molecules of water and surrounding materials.

   c. It prevents water from moving through materials with pores.

   d. It causes clothing to stay dry.

6. How does capillary action allow water to climb up the sides of a straw?

_____

_____

_____

▶ **Water, the Universal Solvent** (pages 277–278)

7. A mixture that forms when one substance dissolves another is called

   a(n) _____. The substance that does the dissolving is

   called a(n) _____.

Science Explorer *Focus on Earth Science*

8. Why can water dissolve many substances? _____

_____

_____

_____

9. Circle the letter of each substance that dissolves in water.

    a. salt   **b.** oil   **c.** oxygen   **d.** wax

▶ Changing State (pages 278–280)

10. List the three states of matter.

    a. _____ **b.** _____ **c.** _____

11. Solid water is called _____ .

12. Complete the compare/contrast table.

How Water Changes State		
Type of Change	**Starting State**	**Ending State**
Melting	Solid	Liquid
Boiling		
Evaporation		
Condensation		
Freezing		

13. The measurement of the average speed of molecules is called

    _____ .

Match the state of water with the statement that is true about it.

    State of Water   **Statement**

    _____ **14.** ice   **a.** It is invisible.

    _____ **15.** liquid water   **b.** It takes the shape of its container.

    _____ **16.** water vapor   **c.** It has a temperature less than 0°C.

© Prentice-Hall, Inc.

CHAPTER 9, Earth: The Water Planet *(continued)*

17. Circle the letter of each sentence that is true about evaporation.

    a. It occurs as water molecules absorb energy.

    b. It occurs as water molecules slow down.

    c. It occurs at the surface of a liquid.

    d. An example of it is air drying your hair after swimming.

18. Circle the letter of each sentence that is true about condensation.

    a. It occurs as water molecules slow down.

    b. It occurs as the temperature of water molecules reaches the boiling point.

    c. It turns water from a visible state to an invisible state.

    d. An example of it is clouding up a cold window with your breath.

▶ Why Ice Floats (page 280)

19. Circle the letter of each sentence that is true about ice.

    a. It has a gridlike crystal structure.

    b. It is less dense than liquid water.

    c. It takes up less space than liquid water.

    d. It protects fish in winter.

▶ Specific Heat (page 281)

20. The amount of heat needed to increase the temperature of a certain

    mass of a substance by 1°C is its _____.

21. Is the following sentence true or false? Compared with other substances, water requires a lot of heat to increase its temperature.

    _____

22. Circle the letter of each sentence that is true about water's specific heat.

    a. It is due to the many attractions among water molecules.

    b. It makes large bodies of water heat up more quickly than nearby land.

    c. It makes large bodies of water cool off more slowly than nearby land.

    d. It leads to warmer air over land than over water on summer days.

Science Explorer *Focus on Earth Science*

Reading Skill Practice

When you read a section with difficult material, turning the headings into questions and then trying to find the answers can help you focus on the most important points. For each heading in Section 9-2, first write the heading as a how, what, or why question, and then find and write the answer to your question. Do your work on a separate sheet of paper.

SECTION 9–3 **The Water Cycle** (pages 284–287)

This section describes the water cycle, a series of processes that moves water from Earth's surface to the atmosphere and back to Earth's surface again in a continuous cycle.

▶ Introduction (page 284)

1. Circle the letter of each sentence that is true about the water cycle.

    a. It naturally recycles water.

    b. It is powered by energy from the sun.

    c. It is a continuous process.

    d. It does not involve living things.

2. Is the following sentence true or false? All the water on Earth has been

    through the water cycle. _____

▶ Water Evaporates (pages 284–286)

3. Is the following sentence true or false? The water cycle has a beginning

    and an end. _____

4. How do plants take in water? _____

    _____

5. Is the following sentence true or false? Plants give off only a small

    amount of water. _____

CHAPTER 9, Earth: The Water Planet (continued)

6. Add arrows to the diagram to show how water moves through the water cycle.

The Water Cycle

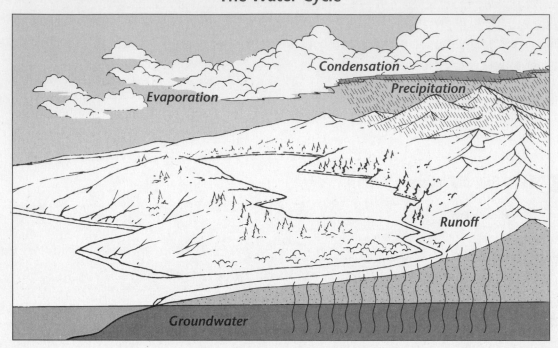

7. Why isn't water vapor that comes from the ocean salty? _____

_____

8. Complete the table.

Processes in the Water Cycle	
Process	**Role in the Water Cycle**
Evaporation	Produces water vapor from bodies of water
	Produces water vapor from plants
	Forms clouds from water vapor
	Returns water to Earth's surface

▶ Clouds Form (page 286)

9. Why does water vapor condense when it travels far above Earth?

_____

_____

10. Describe how clouds form. _____

_____

_____

▶ Water Falls As Precipitation (pages 286–287)

11. How does precipitation occur? _____

_____

_____

12. List four forms of precipitation.

    a. _____   **b.** _____

    c. _____   **d.** _____

13. Is the following sentence true or false? Little precipitation actually falls

directly into the oceans. _____

14. Circle the letter of each sentence that is true about groundwater.

    a. It may move underground to join a river, lake, or ocean.

    b. It must reach the surface to continue through the water cycle.

    c. It must evaporate to continue through the water cycle.

    d. It continues through the water cycle as runoff.

15. Is the following sentence true or false? Water that is taken in by animals

is no longer part of the water cycle. _____

▶ A Global Process (page 287)

16. Circle the letter of each sentence that is true about the Earth's water supply.

    a. Precipitation is the source of all fresh water on Earth.

    b. The water cycle uses up Earth's fresh water supply.

    c. Earth's total water supply has decreased greatly over the past million
    years.

    d. In the world as a whole, rates of evaporation and precipitation are
    balanced.

CHAPTER 9, Earth: The Water Planet *(continued)*

WordWise

Test your knowledge of key terms from Chapter 9 by completing the crossword puzzle.

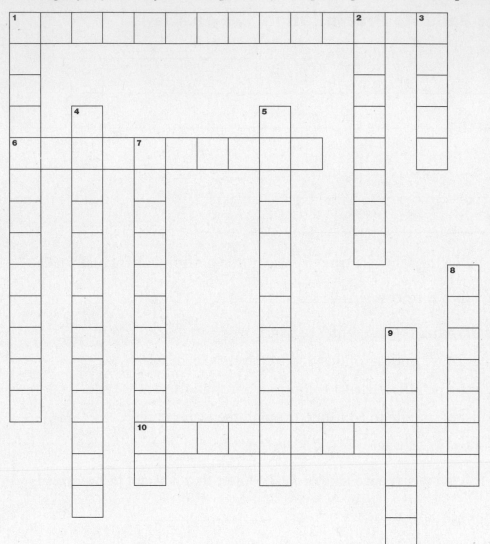

Clues down

1. Water that falls from clouds
2. Mixture of one substance dissolved in another
3. Form of matter
4. Process by which plants release water vapor
5. Process by which water vapor changes to liquid water
7. Water in underground soil and rock layers
8. Substance that dissolves another substance
9. Place where an organism lives

Clues across

1. Process by which plants make food
6. Process of supplying water to the land for growing crops
10. Process by which liquid water changes to water vapor

CHAPTER 10

FRESH WATER

....

SECTION 10-1 ## Streams and Rivers
(pages 294-304)

This section describes how streams and rivers begin and how they shape the land. It also describes systems of rivers and features of rivers. In addition, the section explains why floods occur and how floods can be controlled.

▶ How Do Rivers Begin? (page 295)

1. How do rivers begin? _____

_____

_____

2. When rain falls, water that flows over the ground surface is called

_____.

3. Complete the concept map.

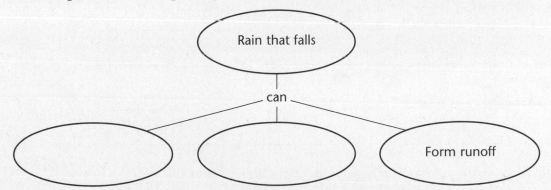

▶ Factors That Affect Runoff (page 295)

4. What factors influence whether water soaks into the ground or flows as

runoff? _____

_____

© Prentice-Hall, Inc.

CHAPTER 10, Fresh Water *(continued)*

5. Circle the letter of each factor that would decrease runoff.

    a. pavement   **b.** grass   **c.** heavy rain   **d.** hilly land

▶ River Systems (pages 296–297)

Match the term with its definition.

Term	Definition
_____ **6.** tributary	**a.** A river and all its tributaries together
_____ **7.** river system	**b.** The land area that supplies water to a river system
_____ **8.** watershed	**c.** A smaller stream or river that feeds into a main river
_____ **9.** divide	**d.** The ridge that separates one watershed from another

▶ Rivers Shape the Land (pages 297–299)

10. Complete the compare/contrast table.

Processes That Shape the Land	
Process	**Description**
	Process in which sediment is carried away
	Process in which sediment is left behind

11. How do rivers shape the land? _____

_____

12. Is the following sentence true or false? The faster a river flows, the

greater its ability to erode the land. _____

▶ Profile of a River (pages 300–302)

13. The many small streams that come together at the source of a river are

called the _____.

14. The broad, flat valley through which a river flows is called the

_____. Looping curves in a river formed by erosion and

deposition are called _____.

15. Number the pictures to show the correct sequence in which an oxbow
lake forms.

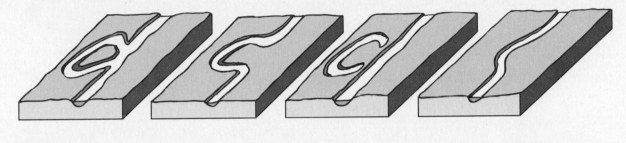

_____   _____   _____   _____

16. The point of a river where it flows into another body of water is called

the _____.

17. Deposits at the mouth of a river build up to form a(n) _____.

▶ **Rivers and Floods** (page 303)

18. When does a flood occur? _____

_____

_____

19. Why have people both feared and welcomed floods? _____

_____

_____

▶ **Can Floods Be Controlled?** (page 304)

20. How can dams help to control floods? _____

_____

21. Long ridges of sediments alongside the channel of a river are called

_____.

CHAPTER 10, Fresh Water *(continued)*

Ponds and Lakes
(pages 305-310)

This section describes ponds and lakes, including how lakes form and the habitats lakes provide. The section also explains why a lake changes over time.

▶ **Introduction** (page 305)

1. Complete the Venn diagram by labeling each circle.

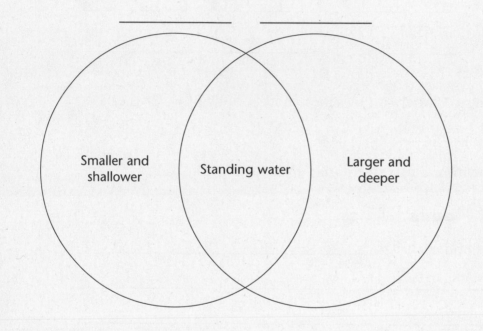

2. When do ponds and lakes form? _____

_____

_____

▶ **Ponds** (pages 306–307)

3. Circle the letter of each sentence that is true about ponds.

   a. Ponds provide only one type of habitat.

   b. All ponds exist year-round.

   c. Algae are the basic food producers in ponds.

   d. Pond animals include fish.

4. Circle the letter of the sentence that explains why plants grow throughout a pond.

　a. Pond water is shallow.　　　**b.** Animals live throughout a pond.

　c. A pond is muddy on the bottom.　**d.** Algae grow in a pond.

▶ Lakes (pages 307–309)

5. Is the following sentence true or false? Lakes form in many ways.

_____

6. Circle the letter of the sentence that explains how Lake Victoria in central Africa formed.

　a. A river meander was cut off to form an oxbow lake.

　b. Movements in Earth's crust created a valley that filled with water.

　c. Lava from a volcano dammed up a river and formed a lake.

　d. An empty volcanic crater filled with water.

7. What are ways a lake may be used by people? _____

_____

_____

8. A lake that stores water for human use is called a(n) _____.

9. Is the following sentence true or false? Wildlife near the shore in a lake is similar to wildlife in a pond. _____

10. Is the following sentence true or false? Compared with the center of a pond, the center of a lake has more organisms. _____

▶ Changes in a Lake (pages 309–310)

11. Circle the letter of each sentence that is true about lake turnover.

　a. It occurs in cool northern areas of North America.

　b. It happens each year.

　c. It occurs in the summer.

　d. It causes nutrients to rise from the bottom to the surface.

CHAPTER 10, Fresh Water *(continued)*

12. Circle the letter of each sentence that is true about eutrophication.

    a. It happens over a long period of time.

    b. It causes more algae to grow in a lake.

    c. It is a process of using up nutrients in a lake.

    d. It keeps lake water clear.

· ·

SECTION 10-3 **Wetland Environments** (pages 311-316)

This section describes what wetlands are and the habitats they provide. The section also explains why wetlands are important and why the Everglades, a wetland region in Florida, is a unique environment.

▶ **What Is a Wetland?** (pages 311-313)

1. Circle the letter of each sentence that is true about a wetland.

    a. It is an area of land covered with shallow water.

    b. It can be small or large.

    c. It may dry up in the summer.

    d. It may form where groundwater seeps onto the surface.

2. Complete the concept map.

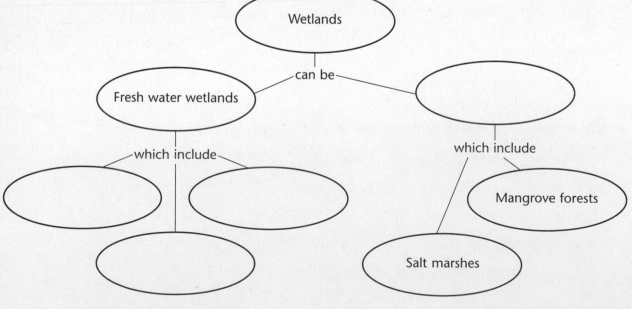

Match the type of wetland with its description.

Type of Wetland	Description
_____ 3. marsh	a. It has trees and shrubs growing in the water.
_____ 4. swamp	b. It has tall, strong grasses and a rich, muddy bottom.
_____ 5. bog	c. It has cattails, rushes, and other tall grass-like plants.
_____ 6. salt marsh	d. It has short trees with a thick tangle of roots.
_____ 7. mangrove forest	e. It has acidic water and mosses.

▶ Wetland Habitats (page 313)

8. Circle the letter of each sentence that is true about wetland habitats.

   a. They have sheltered waters.

   b. They provide a poor supply of nutrients.

   c. They have very different animal life from other freshwater habitats.

   d. They have many temporary residents.

▶ The Importance of Wetlands (page 314)

9. Circle the letter of the choice that is a natural function of wetlands.

   a. Helping control floods

   b. Filtering water

   c. Trapping silt and mud

   d. Providing farmland

▶ The Everglades: A Unique Environment (pages 315–316)

10. Circle the letter of each sentence that is true about the Everglades.

   a. The water in the Everglades does not flow.

   b. No trees grow in the Everglades.

   c. Many rare and endangered species live in the Everglades.

   d. The Everglades are a fragile environment.

CHAPTER 10, Fresh Water *(continued)*

11. How has development affected the water in the Everglades? _____

_____

_____

• •

SECTION 10-4 | **Glaciers and Icebergs** (pages 317-319)

This section describes how glaciers and icebergs form and where they are found. The section also explains how glaciers shape Earth's surface and why icebergs are a hazard to ships.

▶ **Glaciers** (pages 317–318)

1. A huge mass of ice and snow that moves slowly over the land is a(n)

_____.

2. Is the following sentence true or false? Glaciers form where more snow

melts each year than falls. _____

3. Why do the layers of snow in a glacier turn to ice? _____

_____

_____

4. Complete the concept map.

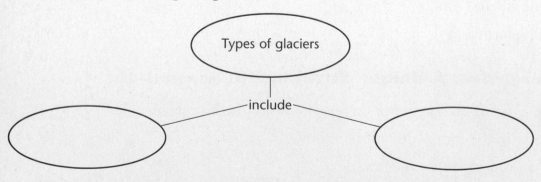

5. Is the following sentence true or false? Today, continental glaciers are

found only in Antarctica. _____

6. Is the following sentence true or false? Most present-day glaciers are

valley glaciers. _____

7. Is the following sentence true or false? As a valley glacier descends into

warmer regions, it spreads out and becomes larger. _____

8. Where are valley glaciers found? _____

_____

_____

9. How does a glacier cause erosion? _____

_____

_____

_____

▶ **Icebergs** (pages 318–319)

10. Large chunks that break off a glacier and float away in the ocean are

called _____.

11. Circle the letter of each sentence that is true about icebergs.

   a. Icebergs are made of frozen salt water.

   b. Many North Atlantic icebergs come from Greenland.

   c. Icebergs are smallest near Antarctica.

   d. About 90 percent of an iceberg is visible above water.

Reading Skill Practice

When you read about related concepts, making a graphic organizer such as a Venn diagram can help you distinguish their similarities and differences. As you read or review Section 10-4, make a Venn diagram that shows some of the similarities and differences between glaciers and icebergs. For more information about Venn diagrams, see page 721 of the Skills Handbook in your textbook. Do your work on a separate sheet of paper.

CHAPTER 10, Fresh Water *(continued)*

· ·

SECTION 10–5 **Water Underground**
(pages 320–326)

This section explains how water gets underground from the surface and how underground water is stored in rock layers. The section also describes how underground water gets back to the surface.

▶ **Underground Layers** (pages 320–321)

1. Precipitation that soaks into the ground trickles downward due to

_____.

Match the term with its definition.

Term	Definition
_____ **2.** pore	**a.** Allows water to pass through
_____ **3.** permeable	**b.** Area that is totally filled with water
_____ **4.** impermeable	**c.** Space between rock and soil particles
_____ **5.** saturated zone	**d.** Does not let water pass through
_____ **6.** water table	**e.** Layer above the water table
_____ **7.** unsaturated zone	**f.** Top of the saturated zone

8. In the drawing, label the water table and the saturated and unsaturated zones.

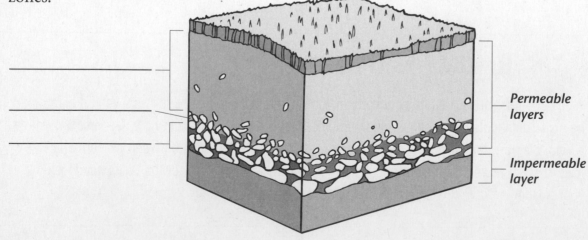

Science Explorer *Focus on Earth Science*

© Prentice-Hall, Inc.

▶ Aquifers (page 324)

9. Any underground layer of rock or sediment that holds water is called

   a(n) _____.

10. Circle the letter of each sentence that is true about aquifers.

    a. All of them are very large.

    b. They can provide drinking water.

    c. They can provide water for crops.

    d. They contain moving water.

▶ Bringing Groundwater to the Surface (pages 324–325)

11. Is the following sentence true or false? The depth of the water table is

    always the same, even over a large area of land. _____

12. Circle the letter of the choice that best explains how to get water from
    an aquifer with a well.

    a. By drilling below the water table

    b. By drilling below the aquifer

    c. By drilling through impermeable rock

    d. By drilling near a dry well

13. New water that enters an aquifer from the surface is called

    _____.

14. A well in which water rises because of pressure within an aquifer is

    called a(n) _____.

▶ Springs and Geysers (pages 325–326)

15. Places where groundwater bubbles or flows out of cracks in the rock are

    called _____.

16. A type of hot spring from which the water bursts periodically into the

    air is called a(n) _____.

CHAPTER 10, Fresh Water *(continued)*

WordWise

Match each definition in the left column with the correct term in the right column. Then write the number of each term in the appropriate box below. When you have filled in all the boxes, add up the numbers in each column, row, and two diagonals. All the sums should be the same.

A. Huge mass of ice and snow that moves slowly over land

B. Long ridge of sediments deposited alongside a river channel

C. Layer of permeable rock or soil that is saturated with water

D. Top of the saturated zone

E. Area covered with shallow water some or all of the year

F. Broad, flat valley through which a river flows

G. Land area that supplies water to a river system

H. New water that enters an aquifer from the surface

I. Process by which nutrients in a lake build up

1. levee
2. watershed
3. flood plain
4. eutrophication
5. wetland
6. glacier
7. water table
8. saturated zone
9. recharge

A ____	B ____	C ____
D ____	E ____	F ____
G ____	H ____	I ____

= ____

= ____

= ____

= ____

= ____   = ____   = ____

____   ____   ____

= ____

CHAPTER 11

FRESHWATER RESOURCES

© Prentice-Hall, Inc.

SECTION 11–1 **Water to Drink** (pages 332–341)

This section describes sources of drinking water, how drinking water is treated to make it safe, and how it is distributed to homes and businesses. The section also describes how wastewater is treated so it can be returned safely to the environment.

▶ Sources of Drinking Water (page 333)

1. Circle the letter of each choice that is an important source of drinking water in the United States.

   a. rivers   **b.** lakes   **c.** reservoirs   **d.** oceans

2. Most people in rural areas of the United States get their drinking water

   from _____.

3. How do large communities maintain public water supplies? _____

   _____

▶ Treating Drinking Water (pages 333–336)

4. A measurement of the substances in water besides water molecules is

   referred to as _____.

5. Is the following sentence true or false? The pH of water is a

   measurement of how acidic or basic the water is. _____

6. Is the following sentence true or false? The higher the pH, the more

   acidic the water. _____

7. How can acidic water cause problems? _____

   _____

CHAPTER 11, Freshwater Resources (continued)

8. The level of calcium and magnesium in water is referred to as

   _____.

9. What is the main problem with hard water for most people? _____

   _____

10. What does the coliform count measure? _____

    _____

11. Is the following sentence true or false? A high coliform count is a sign
    that the water may contain more than one kind of disease-causing

    organism. _____

12. The amount of one substance in a certain volume of another substance

    is its _____.

13. Is the following sentence true or false? EPA water-quality standards
    allow drinking water to contain only water molecules.

    _____

▶ A Typical Treatment Plant (pages 337–338)

14. Add arrows to the drawing to show the direction in which water moves
    through a water treatment plant.

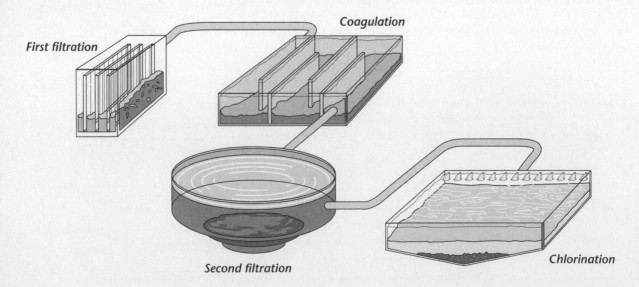

First filtration

Coagulation

Second filtration

Chlorination

© Prentice-Hall, Inc.

15. When alum is added to water, sticky globs, called _____, form.

Match the step in the water treatment process with its description.

Step	Description
_____ **16.** filtration	**a.** Water is treated to create flocs.
_____ **17.** coagulation	**b.** Water is treated to kill microorganisms.
_____ **18.** chlorination	**c.** Water is passed through screens to remove objects.

▶ Water Distribution (pages 338–339)

19. Circle the letter of the choice that shows the correct sequence that water follows after it has been treated.

   a. Small pipes, central pumping station, water mains

   b. Central pumping station, water mains, small pipes

   c. Water mains, small pipes, central pumping station

   d. Central pumping station, small pipes, water mains

20. What causes the water to move through a community's system of

underground water pipes? _____

_____

_____

▶ Treating Wastewater (pages 339–341)

21. Sewage is carried away from homes by _____.

22. Complete the table.

Wastewater Terms	
Term	**What It Means**
	Wastewater and the different kinds of wastes that it contains
	Deposits of fine solids that settle out from wastewater
	Treated wastewater that you cannot drink

CHAPTER 11, Freshwater Resources *(continued)*

▶ Septic Systems (page 341)

23. An underground tank containing bacteria that treat wastewater is called

a(n) _____.

24. The area of ground in a septic system that the water filters through is

called a(n) _____.

● ●

SECTION 11-2 # Balancing Water Needs
(pages 342-346)

This section explains how the supply of water and the demand for water can change.
The section also describes ways to conserve water and new ways of obtaining fresh
water that may be used in the future.

▶ Water Supply and Demand (pages 343–344)

1. Is the following sentence true or false? Water is a nonrenewable

resource. _____

2. When does a water shortage occur? _____

_____

_____

3. The condition of scarce rainfall for a few years is known as a(n)

_____.

4. Circle the letter of each sentence that is true about droughts.

a. They affect the supply of surface water.

b. They affect the supply of groundwater.

c. They cause the water table to rise.

d. They may cause wells to run dry.

5. How can an aquifer be recharged naturally after a drought? _____

_____

Science Explorer *Focus on Earth Science*

▶ Conserving Water (pages 344–345)

6. Using a resource wisely so that it will not be used up is called

_____.

7. Circle the letter of each choice that helps conserve water in the home.

    a. Taking shorter showers

    b. Watering the lawn around noon instead of early or late in the day

    c. Keeping a pitcher of drinking water in the refrigerator

    d. Running the washing machine only when you have small loads

8. Is the following sentence true or false? In the United States, the biggest

use of water is for agriculture. _____

9. How do sprinkler and drip irrigation systems help conserve water?

_____

10. Complete the concept map.

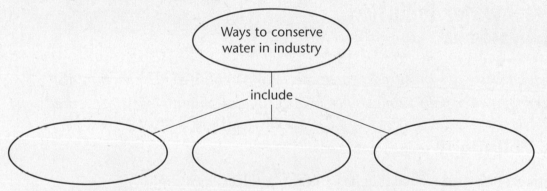

▶ Fresh Water for the Future (pages 345–346)

11. Circle the letter of the choice that gives the correct sequence of steps in distillation.

    a. Evaporation, boiling, condensation

    b. Boiling, condensation, evaporation

    c. Boiling, evaporation, condensation

    d. Condensation, boiling, evaporation

12. The process of obtaining fresh water from salt water is called

_____.

CHAPTER 11, Freshwater Resources *(continued)*

13. How could an iceberg be used to supply fresh water to a dry region on

the coast of Africa or South America? _____

_____

_____

_____

14. What environmental questions have been raised about using icebergs

for fresh water? _____

_____

_____

_____

· ·

SECTION 11–3

Freshwater Pollution
(pages 349–356)

This section describes ways that fresh water can become polluted. The section also describes how freshwater pollution can be cleaned up and how it can be prevented.

▶ What Is Pollution? (pages 349–350)

1. The addition of any substance that has a negative effect on water or the

living things that depend on the water is called _____.

2. Circle the letter of each sentence that is true about water pollution.

   a. It can affect surface water.

   b. It cannot affect groundwater.

   c. It results from human activities.

   d. It does not result from natural causes.

3. The substances that cause pollution are called _____.

4. What are some types of pollutants found in water? _____

_____

_____

5. Is the following sentence true or false? It is safe to bathe or swim in

polluted water as long as you do not drink it. _____

▶ Point and Nonpoint Sources (pages 350–351)

6. List the four major sources of water pollution.

a. _____   b. _____

c. _____   d. _____

7. What is the difference between a point source and a nonpoint source of

water pollution? _____

_____

_____

▶ Human Wastes (pages 351–352)

8. How can a flood cause polluted surface water? _____

_____

_____

9. Is the following sentence true or false? Disposing of human waste is a

problem only in big cities. _____

10. Complete the concept map.

Types of industrial pollutants

include

( )   ( )   ( )

CHAPTER 11, Freshwater Resources *(continued)*

11. Circle the letter of each sentence that is true about toxic chemical wastes from industry.

   a. Few industrial processes involve toxic chemicals.

   b. Some toxic wastes are side effects of manufacturing and mining.

   c. Chemical pollution from factories is now controlled by law.

   d. Factories no longer release toxic chemicals directly into rivers and lakes.

12. Rain that is more acidic than normal is called _____.

13. Circle the letter of each sentence that is an outcome of acid rain.

   a. Fish die off.

   b. Groundwater is polluted with oil and gasoline.

   c. Stone buildings and statues are eaten away.

   d. Lake water becomes acidic.

14. How could warm water act like a pollutant? _____

_____

_____

_____

▶ Agricultural Chemicals (page 354)

15. Is the following sentence true or false? Fertilizers in runoff water are a

   point source of pollution. _____

16. Chemicals intended to kill insects and other organisms that damage

   crops are called _____.

▶ Runoff from Roads (page 354)

17. List three pollutants that are found in runoff from roads.

   a. _____   **b.** _____   **c.** _____

18. Is the following sentence true or false? Road runoff is a nonpoint

   source of pollution. _____

© Prentice-Hall, Inc.

▶ **Cleaning Up Polluted Water** (page 355)

19. Circle the letter of each sentence that describes a way that polluted fresh water is cleaned naturally.

  a. Runoff waters from farm fields dilute the pollution in rivers and lakes.

  b. Plants absorb metals and chemicals from lake and pond water.

  c. Bacteria eat toxic chemicals and oil spills.

  d. Sand and rock layers filter groundwater as it flows down through them.

▶ **Preventing Pollution** (pages 355–356)

20. Is the following sentence true or false? Most pollutants are not very difficult to remove. _____

21. Is the following sentence true or false? It is often easier to avoid causing pollution in the first place than to clean it up. _____

22. Describe some ways that industry and agriculture can help lessen pollution. _____

_____

_____

_____

· ·

SECTION 11-4 **Water As an Energy Resource** (pages 357-360)

This section describes how water moving over a waterfall or dam can be used to generate electricity. The section also identifies some of the benefits and drawbacks of building dams.

▶ **Power from Moving Water** (pages 357–358)

1. Electricity produced by water moving over a waterfall or dam is called

_____.

CHAPTER 11, Freshwater Resources *(continued)*

2. Complete the Venn diagram by labeling each circle with the type of energy it represents.

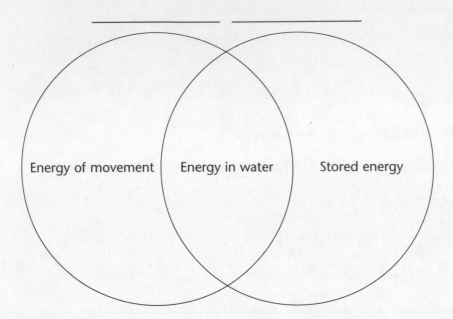

_____ _____

Energy of movement   Energy in water   Stored energy

Match the part of a hydroelectric power plant with how it converts energy.

Part of Hydroelectric Plant   **How It Converts Energy**

_____ 3. floodgate

_____ 4. turbine

_____ 5. generator

a. Converts mechanical energy to electrical energy

b. Converts kinetic energy to mechanical energy

c. Converts potential energy to kinetic energy

▶ The Impact of Dams (pages 358–360)

6. Circle the letter of each sentence that is true about hydroelectric power.

   a. It is clean.

   b. It is efficient.

   c. It is safe.

   d. It causes air pollution.

7. Is the following sentence true or false? Hydroelectric power can be

   generated by any source of moving water. _____

8. Circle the letter of each sentence that describes how dams affect the environment.

   a. Dams destroy wildlife habitats.

   b. Dams prevent fish from swimming upstream.

   c. Dams increase fish populations.

   d. Dams enrich farmlands downstream.

9. Is the following sentence true or false? Dams increase the erosion caused by fast-moving rivers. _____

10. Is the following sentence true or false? Water power is the least expensive and least polluting large-scale energy source. _____

11. Besides supplying power for electricity, list two benefits of dams.

   a. _____

   b. _____

12. What are the pros and cons of building small dams to supply power to local areas? _____

_____

_____

_____

_____

📖 Reading Skill Practice

When you read about a complex process, studying an illustration of the process may help you understand it. Carefully study the drawing of the hydroelectric plant in the Exploring feature on page 359. Then summarize in your own words how electricity is produced in a hydroelectric plant. Do your work on a separate sheet of paper.

CHAPTER 11, Freshwater Resources (continued)

WordWise

Solve the clues with key terms from Chapter 11. Then put the numbered letters in order to reveal the message.

Clues   **Key Terms**

1. Level of calcium and magnesium in water

   _ _ _ _ _ _ _
   1   2

2. Sticky globs created during water treatment

   _ _ _ _ _
      3

3. Chemical intended to kill insects or other pests

   _ _ _ _ _ _ _ _ _
   4   5

4. Amount of one substance in a certain volume of another

   _ _ _ _ _ _ _ _ _ _ _ _ _
     6 7

5. Type of underground tank that contains bacteria for treating wastewater

   _ _ _ _ _ _
   8 9

6. Using a resource wisely

   _ _ _ _ _ _ _ _ _ _ _ _
           10 11

7. Sediments that settle out during water treatment

   _ _ _ _ _ _
       12

8. Water containing human wastes

   _ _ _ _ _ _
     13 14

9. Process of passing water through screens to remove objects

   _ _ _ _ _ _ _ _ _
      15

10. Process of removing salt from water

    _ _ _ _ _ _ _ _ _ _ _
    16

11. Water shortage due to long periods of low precipitation

    _ _ _ _ _ _ _
    17

Hidden Message

_ _ _ _   _ _ _ _ _ _ _ _
1 2 3 4   5 6 7 8 9 10 11 12

_ _ _ _ _ .
13 14 15 16 17

CHAPTER 12

OCEAN MOTIONS

....

SECTION 12-1 **Wave Action** (pages 366-373)

This section explains how waves form and how they change near shore. The section also describes how waves affect the shore and how wave erosion can be reduced.

▶ How Waves Form (pages 366–368)

1. The movement of energy through a body of water is a(n)

   _____.

2. How do most waves form? _____

   _____

   _____

3. Is the following sentence true or false? Waves start in the open ocean.

   _____

4. Circle the letter of each choice that determines the size of a wave.

   a. Strength of the wind   **b.** How long the wind blows

   c. How far the wind blows   **d.** Amount of water the wave carries

5. Is the following sentence true or false? Water is moved toward shore by a

   wave. _____

6. Circle the letter of the sentence that describes what happens to water particles near the surface when a wave passes by.

   a. The water particles move toward shore.

   b. The water particles move in circles.

   c. The water particles move randomly.

   d. The water particles move little if at all.

CHAPTER 12, Ocean Motions *(continued)*

7. Circle the letter of the sentence that describes what happens to water particles in deep water when a wave passes by.

   a. The water particles move away from shore.

   b. The water particles move in large circles.

   c. The water particles move randomly.

   d. The water particles move little if at all.

▶ **Describing Waves** (pages 368–369)

Match the term with its definition.

Term	Definition
_____ **8.** wavelength	**a.** Horizontal distance between crests
_____ **9.** frequency	**b.** Vertical distance from crest to trough
_____ **10.** wave height	**c.** Number of waves that pass a point in a certain amount of time

11. Label a crest and a trough in the drawing of waves.

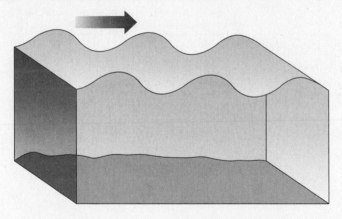

12. Is the following sentence true or false? The energy of a wave depends mainly on its wavelength. _____

▶ **How Waves Change Near Shore** (page 369)

13. As a wave approaches shore, what happens to wave height and

    wavelength? _____

    _____

14. How is surf formed? _____

_____

_____

15. Water that moves up the beach in a wave flows back out to sea due to

_____.

▶ How Waves Affect the Shore (page 370)

Match the term with its description.

Term	Description
_____ **16.** longshore drift	**a.** Underwater ridge of sand
_____ **17.** sandbar	**b.** Movement of sand along a beach
_____ **18.** rip current	**c.** Rapid rush of water out to sea

▶ Waves and Beach Erosion (page 371)

19. How do waves shape a beach? _____

_____

▶ Reducing Erosion (pages 371–372)

20. A wall of rocks or concrete built outward from a beach to stop

longshore drift is called a(n) _____.

21. Hills of wind-blown sand covered with plants are called

_____.

▶ Tsunamis (page 373)

22. Circle the letter of the sentence that is true about tsunamis.

a. They are waves.

b. They are most common in the Atlantic Ocean.

c. They are felt most in deep water.

d. They cause earthquakes.

CHAPTER 12, Ocean Motions *(continued)*

📖 Reading Skill Practice

When you read a long section, taking notes can help you identify and remember the most important information. Take notes on Section 12-1 by writing the main headings and under each heading listing the most important points. Include in your notes the bold-faced terms and sentences. Do your work on a separate sheet of paper.

SECTION 12-2 ## Tides *(pages 374-378)*

This section explains what causes tides and describes the daily and monthly cycles of tides. The section also explains how energy in tides can be harnessed.

▶ What Causes Tides? *(page 375)*

1. The daily rise and fall of Earth's water on its coastlines are called

    _____.

2. What is the difference between high tide and low tide? _____

    _____

    _____

3. At which two points are tidal bulges occurring when Earth and the moon are in the positions shown in the drawing? _____

    _____

    _____

    _____

4. Explain why a tidal bulge occurs on the side of Earth opposite the moon.

_____

_____

_____

_____

▶ The Daily Tide Cycle (page 376)

5. Circle the letter of each sentence that is true about high tides.

   a. They occur twice a day.

   b. They occur later in the west.

   c. They occur six hours apart.

   d. They occur more often than low tides.

6. Is the following sentence true or false? High tides occur about twelve

   and a half hours apart. _____

7. What factors affect the height of the tide in any particular location?

_____

_____

▶ The Monthly Tide Cycle (pages 376–377)

8. Is the following sentence true or false? The sun's gravity affects Earth's

   tides. _____

9. Complete the compare/contrast table with the following terms: least, greatest, neap tide, spring tide.

Monthly Tide Cycle		
Type of Tide	**Position of Sun and Moon**	**Difference Between High and Low Tides**
	Sun and moon in straight line	
	Sun and moon at right angles	

CHAPTER 12, Ocean Motions (continued)

10. Circle the letter of each sentence that is true about spring tides.

   a. They occur twice a month.

   b. They occur only in spring.

   c. They occur during a new moon.

   d. They occur during a full moon.

11. Who needs to know the times and heights of tides? _____

   _____

   _____

▶ Energy From Tides (page 378)

12. Is the following sentence true or false? The energy stored in tides is

   potential energy. _____

13. Describe how a tidal power plant captures tidal energy. _____

   _____

   _____

   _____

14. Circle the letter of the sentence that is true about tidal energy.

   a. It is clean.   **b.** It is nonrenewable.

   c. It can be used on any coast.   **d.** It cannot be harnessed.

SECTION 12–3 Ocean Water Chemistry (pages 379–383)

This section describes the saltiness of ocean water and the gases that ocean water contains. The section also describes how temperature, pressure, and other properties of ocean water change as you go deeper in the ocean.

▶ The Salty Ocean (pages 379–381)

1. The total amount of dissolved salts in water is called _____.

2. Label the two parts of the circle graph.

Composition of Ocean Water

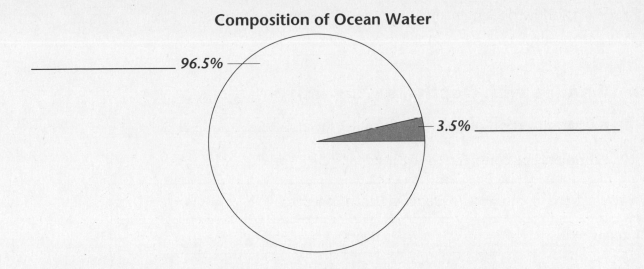

_____ 96.5%

3.5% _____

3. Circle the letter of each place in the ocean where salinity is likely to be relatively low.

   a. Near melting ice   **b.** Near the mouth of a large river

   c. Where the climate is hot and dry   **d.** Near the poles

4. Circle the letter of the sentence that is true about the effect of salinity on ocean water.

   a. Salinity increases the freezing point of ocean water.

   b. Salinity decreases the density of ocean water.

   c. Salinity decreases the mass of ocean water.

   d. Salinity increases the buoyancy of ocean water.

▶ Gases in Ocean Water (page 381)

5. List two gases found in ocean water that are necessary for living things.

   a. _____   **b.** _____

6. Is the following sentence true or false? There is more oxygen in seawater

than in air. _____

▶ The Temperature of Ocean Water (page 381)

7. Why does warm water stay at the surface of the ocean? _____

_____

CHAPTER 12, Ocean Motions *(continued)*

8. Is the following sentence true or false? Warm water contains more

dissolved oxygen than cold water. _____

▶ Changes with Depth (pages 382–383)

9. A vertical section of the ocean is called the _____.

10. Complete the compare/contrast table.

Depth of Ocean Zones	
Zone	**Depth**
	Begins at about 1 kilometer below the surface
	Extends to about 200 meters below the surface
	Extends to about 1 kilometer below the surface

11. Circle the letter of each sentence that is true about temperature in the ocean.

  a. Temperature decreases as depth increases.

  b. Temperature is highest in the transition zone.

  c. Temperature drops quickly in the surface zone.

  d. Temperature is lowest in the deep zone.

12. Is the following sentence true or false? Below the surface zone, the

salinity of ocean water remains fairly constant. _____

13. Circle the letter of each sentence that is true about pressure in the ocean.

  a. Pressure is the weight of the water above pressing down.

  b. Pressure rises continuously as depth increases.

  c. Pressure on the ocean floor is twice as great as pressure at sea level.

  d. A diver can safely withstand pressure at 1 kilometer below sea level.

14. An underwater vehicle built to resist pressure is called a(n)

_____.

© Prentice-Hall, Inc.

SECTION 12-4 Currents and Climate
(pages 386-392)

This section describes surface and deep ocean currents and explains how they affect climate.

▶ **Introduction** (pages 386–387)

1. A large stream of moving water that flows through the oceans is a(n)

   _____.

2. Is the following sentence true or false? Currents carry water great

   distances. _____

▶ **Surface Currents** (pages 387–388)

3. Circle the letter of each sentence that is true about surface currents.

   a. They affect water down to 1 kilometer.

   b. They are driven mainly by winds.

   c. They move in circular patterns.

   d. They occur only in the Pacific Ocean.

4. The effect of Earth's rotation on the direction of winds and currents is

   called the _____.

5. Is the following sentence true or false? In the Northern Hemisphere,

   surface currents curve to the left. _____

6. The largest and most powerful surface current in the North Atlantic

   Ocean is the _____.

7. Circle the letter of the sentence that is true about the Gulf Stream.

   a. It is caused by strong winds from the north.

   b. It carries more water than the Mississippi River.

   c. It is a cold-water current.

   d. It curves westward due to the Coriolis effect.

© Prentice-Hall, Inc.

CHAPTER 12, Ocean Motions *(continued)*

8. Is the following sentence true or false? In the Southern Hemisphere,

    surface currents curve to the left. _____

▶ How Surface Currents Affect Climate (page 388)

9. The pattern of temperature and precipitation typical of an area over a

    long period of time is called _____.

10. How does the Gulf Stream influence the climate along the western coast

    of Norway? _____

    _____

    _____

11. How do cold-water currents affect weather on land near a coast?

    _____

    _____

▶ Deep Currents (pages 388–389)

12. Deep currents are caused by differences in _____.

13. The density of water depends on its _____ and its

    _____.

14. Why does water get denser as it moves toward the poles? _____

    _____

    _____

15. Is the following sentence true or false? Deep ocean currents move and

    mix water around the world. _____

▶ Upwelling (pages 389–390)

16. The upward movement of cold water from the ocean depths is referred

    to as _____.

17. Is the following sentence true or false? Upwelling is caused by tides.

_____

18. Label the drawing to show where upwelling occurs.

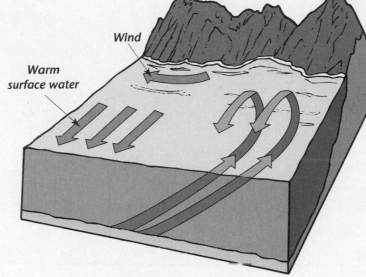

Wind

Warm surface water

19. Why are upwelling zones usually home to enormous schools of fish?

_____

_____

_____

▶ El Niño (pages 391–392)

20. An abnormal climate event that occurs every 2 to 7 years in the Pacific

Ocean is called _____.

21. How does El Niño begin? _____

_____

_____

_____

22. Circle the letter of each sentence that is true about El Niño.

    a. It can prevent upwelling.   **b.** It can affect weather worldwide.

    c. It is fully understood.   **d.** Its impact can be reduced.

CHAPTER 12, Ocean Motions *(continued)*

WordWise

Use the clues to help you unscramble the key terms from Chapter 12. Then put the numbered letters in order to find the answer to the riddle.

Clues	Key Terms	
1. Structure that reduces erosion	rongi	_ _ _ _ _ 1
2. Highest point of a wave	rtecs	_ _ _ _ _ 2
3. Ridge of sand near shore	nasdrab	_ _ _ _ _ _ _ 3
4. Distance between two crests	telegawvnh	_ _ _ _ _ _ _ _ _ _ 4
5. Daily rise and fall of water	sdeit	_ _ _ _ _ 5
6. Saltiness of water	lstainyi	_ _ _ _ _ _ _ _ 6
7. Number of waves passing by in a given time	curenqefy	_ _ _ _ _ _ _ _ _ 7

Riddle: What causes tides?

Answer: _ _ _ _ _ _ _
    1 2 3 4 5 6 7

Science Explorer *Focus on Earth Science*

CHAPTER 13

Ocean Zones

....

Exploring the Ocean (pages 398-406)

This section describes how the ocean has been explored over the past several thousand years. The section also describes features of the ocean floor and explains how the ocean floor moves.

▶ Voyages of Discovery (page 399)

1. Circle the letter of the sentence that is true about the Phoenicians.

   a. They were one of the earliest cultures to explore the oceans.

   b. They sailed to Hawaii.

   c. They established sea routes for trade by 2000 B.C.

   d. They lived on islands in the Indian Ocean.

2. Is the following sentence true or false? Captain Cook's voyages of exploration marked the beginning of the modern science of

   occanography. _____

▶ Exploring the Ocean Floor (pages 399–401)

3. Why has the deep ocean floor been explored only recently? _____

   _____

   _____

   _____

4. Is the following sentence true or false? To study the deep ocean floor, scientists have had to rely on direct methods of gathering information.

   _____

CHAPTER 13, Ocean Zones *(continued)*

5. Circle the letter of each sentence that is true about sonar.

   a. It measures distance.   **b.** It uses sound waves.

   c. It is an indirect way of gathering data.   **d.** It uses X rays.

▶ Features of the Ocean Floor (pages 402–404)

6. Circle the letter of each sentence that is true about the ocean floor.

   a. It is flat and sandy.   **b.** It is rocky and uneven.

   c. It has the biggest mountains on Earth.   **d.** It has deep canyons.

7. Find and label each of the following ocean floor features in the drawing: continental shelf, continental slope, seamount, abyssal plain, and trench.

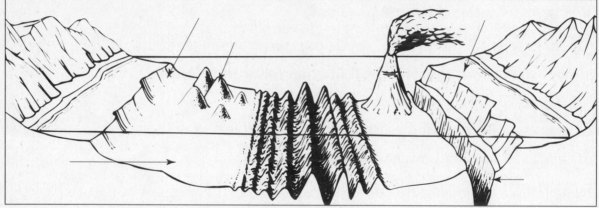

Match each feature of the ocean floor with its description.

Feature

_____ **8.** continental shelf

_____ **9.** continental slope

_____ **10.** seamount

_____ **11.** abyssal plain

_____ **12.** mid-ocean ridge

_____ **13.** trench

Description

a. Smooth and nearly flat region of the ocean floor

b. Mountain on the ocean floor that is completely under water

c. Continuous range of mountains on the ocean floor

d. Incline at the edge of the continental shelf

e. Steep-sided canyon in the ocean floor

f. Shallow area of the ocean floor extending outward from land

14. Circle the letter of each sentence that is true about the mid-ocean ridge.

    a. It passes through all of Earth's oceans.

    b. It is about 800 kilometers long.

    c. It is the longest mountain range on Earth.

    d. It is divided by a central valley.

▶ Movements of the Ocean Floor (pages 404–406)

15. The hot liquid material inside Earth is called _____. If

this material reaches the surface, it is called _____.

16. Pieces of Earth's crust, along with parts of the upper mantle, are called

_____.

17. Circle the letter of each sentence that is true about Earth's plates.

    a. They move on the liquid of the mantle.

    b. They lie beneath the continents but not the oceans.

    c. They move several kilometers per year.

    d. Their movements create Earth's landforms.

18. Describe sea-floor spreading. _____

_____

_____

19. Why doesn't Earth increase in size as the sea-floor spreads along the

mid-ocean ridge? _____

_____

_____

📖 Reading Skill Practice

When you read a long section, writing a summary can help you identify and remember the main ideas. Write a concise paragraph summing up the main ideas under each heading in Section 13-1. Each paragraph should be shorter than the text under that heading in your book. Include each of the boldfaced terms in your summary. Do your work on a separate sheet of paper.

CHAPTER 13, Ocean Zones *(continued)*

• •

Life at the Ocean's Edge (pages 408–413)

This section describes living conditions and types of organisms found in water at the ocean's edge, including along rocky shores and in inlets and bays.

▶ **Living Conditions** (pages 408–410)

1. List physical factors that determine where marine organisms can live.

   a. _____   b. _____   c. _____

   d. _____   e. _____   f. _____

2. Circle the letter of the sentence that is true about how conditions in ocean water vary.

   a. Salinity is higher where rivers flow into the ocean.

   b. Salinity is lower in warm, shallow water.

   c. The level of dissolved gases is higher in cold water.

   d. The level of oxygen in the water does not vary.

3. How do scientists classify marine organisms? _____

   _____

4. Complete the compare/contrast table.

Types of Marine Organisms		
Type of Organism	**Where It Lives**	**How It Moves**
	Near the surface	Floats
	Throughout the water column	Swims freely
	On the ocean floor	Crawls or stays in place

5. Is the following sentence true or false? Many plankton and benthos are algae. _____

6. Circle the letter of each sentence that is true about nekton.

    a. They are animals.   **b.** They include fish and whales.

    c. They are consumers.   **d.** They include algae.

7. Relationships among producers, consumers, and decomposers in a

    habitat make up a _____.

▶ Rocky Shores (pages 410–411)

8. The zone between the highest high-tide line and lowest low-tide line is

    called the _____.

9. What special conditions must organisms tolerate in the rocky intertidal

    zone? _____

    _____

    _____

10. What adaptations do algae have for living in the intertidal zone?

    _____

    _____

    _____

11. Depressions among the rocks that remain filled with water after the tide

    goes out are called _____.

12. Circle the letter of each type of organism you might see in a tide pool.

    a. sea stars   **b.** sea urchins   **c.** sponges   **d.** blackline algae

▶ Where River Meets Ocean (pages 412–413)

13. Coastal inlets or bays where fresh water from rivers mixes with the salty

    ocean water are called _____.

14. Water that is partly salty and partly fresh is referred to as

    _____.

CHAPTER 13, Ocean Zones *(continued)*

15. Complete the Venn diagram.

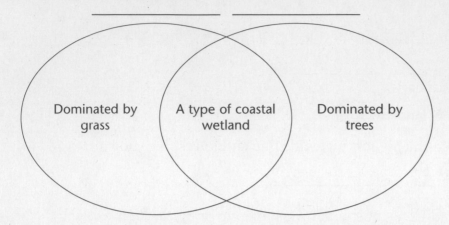

16. How do pollutants enter estuaries, and how are they flushed out?

_____

_____

. . . .

SECTION 13–3 **The Neritic Zone and Open Ocean** (pages 414–420)

This section describes living conditions and types of organisms found in water over the continental shelf and in the open ocean.

▶ **Introduction** (pages 414–415)

1. The part of the ocean that extends from the low-tide line out to the

edge of the continental shelf is called the _____.
The part of the ocean that extends beyond the edge of the continental

shelf is called the _____.

▶ **Conditions in the Neritic Zone** (page 415)

2. Circle the letter of each sentence that helps explain why there is so much life in the neritic zone.

   a. The water is shallow.   **b.** The water is high in nutrients.

   c. Large plantlike algae grow there.   **d.** Upwelling never occurs there.

3. Complete the concept map.

```
                    ┌─────────────────────┐
                    │  Neritic zone habitats │
                    └─────────────────────┘
                              │
                          include
              ╱                           ╲
    ┌──────────────┐              ┌──────────────┐
    │              │              │              │
    └──────────────┘              └──────────────┘
```

▶ Life in a Kelp Forest (page 416)

4. Circle the letter of each sentence that is true about kelp.

   a. They are algae.   **b.** They produce their own food.

   c. They provide food for sea otters.   **d.** They provide a home for slugs.

5. What important role do sea otters play in a kelp forest? _____

_____

_____

_____

▶ Coral Reefs (pages 416–417)

6. Is the following sentence true or false? A coral reef is made of living things.

_____

7. Number the drawings to show the correct sequence of steps in the formation of an atoll.

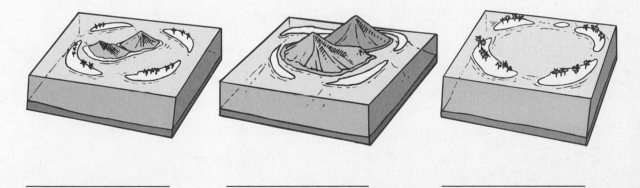

_____   _____   _____

CHAPTER 13, Ocean Zones *(continued)*

Match the type of coral reef with its description.

Type of Reef	Description
_____ 8. atoll	**a.** Reef that is separated from land by a lagoon
_____ 9. fringing reef	**b.** Ring-shaped reef that surrounds a shallow lagoon
_____ 10. barrier reef	**c.** Reef that closely surrounds the edges of an island

11. Is the following sentence true or false? Reefs protect coastlines during

violent storms. _____

▶ Conditions in the Open Ocean (pages 418–419)

12. Is the following sentence true or false? The open ocean supports fewer

organisms than the neritic zone. _____

13. Is the following sentence true or false? The surface zone is the only part of the open ocean that receives enough sunlight to support the growth

of algae. _____

14. How is the deep zone like a desert? _____

_____

15. The production of light by living things is called _____.

▶ Hydrothermal Vents (pages 419–420)

16. An area where heated ocean water rises through cracks in the ocean

floor is a(n) _____.

17. Circle the letter of each sentence that is true about organisms around hydrothermal vents.

    a. Bacteria produce food from chemicals in the hot water.

    b. Tube worms get their food from the bacteria inside them.

    c. Algae form the base of the food web.

    d. Giant clams feed on the algae.

•••

SECTION 13-4 # Resources From the Ocean
(pages 421-426)

This section describes living resources, such as fish, and nonliving resources, such as fuels, that are obtained from the ocean and the ocean floor. The section also explains how the ocean becomes polluted and why Earth's oceans should be protected.

▶ Living Resources (pages 421–423)

1. Is the following sentence true or false? Foods from the ocean make up

   about 10 percent of the world's total food supply. _____

2. List the six species of fish that make up the majority of fishes harvested for eating.

   a. _____   b. _____   c. _____

   d. _____   e. _____   f. _____

3. Where are nearly all fishes caught? _____

   _____

   _____

4. The farming of saltwater and freshwater organisms is called

   _____.

▶ Mineral Resources (pages 423–424)

5. How is magnesium obtained from seawater? _____

   _____

   _____

6. What are some nonliving resources from the ocean floor? _____

   _____

   _____

   _____

CHAPTER 13, Ocean Zones *(continued)*

7. When metals concentrate around pieces of shell on the ocean floor,

   they form black lumps called _____.

8. Is the following sentence true or false? The technology to gather

   nodules was developed in the mid-1900s. _____

9. Circle the letter of the sentence that is true about resources on the deep
   ocean floor.

   a. All nations agree on who owns the rights to the resources.

   b. Everyone agrees that whoever finds the resources should own them.

   c. All nations have the technology to obtain a share of the resources.

   d. Only some nations can afford the technology to obtain the resources.

▶ Fuels From the Ocean Floor (page 424)

10. Is the following sentence true or false? Fuels on the ocean floor come

    from the remains of dead marine organisms. _____

11. Two fuels that are found on the ocean floor are _____

    and _____.

12. Why are the richest deposits of oil and gas often located on the

    continental shelves? _____

    _____

    _____

▶ Ocean Pollution (pages 424–426)

13. Circle the letter of each sentence that is true about ocean pollution.

    a. The ocean is so vast that it cannot become polluted.

    b. Most ocean pollution comes from the land.

    c. The ocean is a self-cleaning system.

    d. Most ocean pollution is due to natural causes.

14. Is the following sentence true or false? Some ocean pollution is the

result of weather. _____

15. How can a sudden surge of fresh water from an estuary pollute the ocean?

_____

_____

_____

16. List three ocean pollutants related to human activities.

a. _____ **b.** _____ **c.** _____

17. Circle the letter of the sentence that is true about oil from oil spills.

a. It is a minor threat to ocean life.

b. It is harmful to only a few organisms.

c. It can destroy an animal's natural insulation.

d. It is harmful only to animals that swallow it.

18. What is the natural cleaning process that slowly takes place after oil spills?

_____

_____

_____

▶ Protecting Earth's Oceans (page 426)

19. Why is it difficult to determine who, if anyone, should control portions

of the ocean? _____

_____

_____

20. Is the following sentence true or false? Approximately three quarters of

the ocean's surface waters are owned by no nation. _____

21. Is the following sentence true or false? Ownership of the ocean floor

beneath the high seas is no longer under debate. _____

CHAPTER 13, Ocean Zones *(continued)*

WordWise

Use the clues to make a list of key terms from Chapter 13. Then find and circle each of the key terms in the hidden-word puzzle. The terms may be written across, down, or diagonally.

Clues	Key Terms
Bundle of rootlike strands that attaches algae to rocks	_____
Device that uses sound waves to measure distance	_____
Deep canyon in the ocean floor	_____
Molten mixture that makes up Earth's mantle	_____
Tiny algae and animals that float in water	_____
Organisms that live on the bottom of the ocean	_____
Habitat in a coastal inlet or bay where fresh and salt water mix	_____
The practice of raising fish and other water organisms for food	_____
Ring-shaped coral island found far from land	_____
Mountain on the ocean floor that is completely under water	_____
Pieces of Earth's crust along with the upper part of the mantle	_____
Water that is partly salty and partly fresh	_____
Free-swimming ocean animals	_____

```
a  c  h  o  l  d  f  a  s  t  h
d  e  s  o  n  a  r  e  f  s  r
t  r  e  n  c  h  t  n  i  h  n
a  m  a  g  m  a  o  k  e  o  b
t  w  m  e  l  t  c  c  t  m  l
o  a  o  p  l  a  n  k  t  o  n
l  l  u  v  r  l  e  n  t  v  l
l  z  n  b  e  n  t  h  o  s  l
e  s  t  u  a  r  y  h  y  d  o
a  q  u  a  c  u  l  t  u  r  e
```

© Prentice-Hall, Inc.

Science Explorer *Focus on Earth Science*

Name _____ Date _____ Class _____

SECTION 14-1	**The Air Around You** (pages 440-443)

This section describes Earth's atmosphere, or the layer of gases that surrounds the planet.

▶ Importance of the Atmosphere (pages 440–441)

1. The condition of Earth's atmosphere at a particular time and place is

   called _____.

2. How does Earth's atmosphere make conditions on Earth suitable for

   living things? _____

   _____

   _____

   _____

   _____

▶ Composition of the Atmosphere (pages 441–443)

3. Label the two larger pieces of the graph with the gases they represent.

Gases in Dry Air

1%
All other gases

CHAPTER 14, The Atmosphere *(continued)*

4. Circle the letter of each sentence that is true about nitrogen.

    a. It is essential to living things.

    b. It is found in proteins.

    c. It is needed for growth and repair of cells.

    d. It is obtained directly from the air by all living things.

5. Circle the letter of each sentence that is true about oxygen.

    a. It is needed by animals but not plants.

    b. It is needed to release energy from food.

    c. It is released by fuels when they burn.

    d. It forms ozone when it interacts with lightning.

6. Circle the letter of each sentence that is true about carbon dioxide.

    a. It is essential to life.

    b. It is given off by animals as a waste product.

    c. It is used by animals to digest food.

    d. It is needed by fuels to burn.

7. Is the following sentence true or false? Carbon dioxide alone makes up almost 1 percent of dry air. _____

8. Water in the form of a gas is called _____.

9. Is the following sentence true or false? Water vapor is the same as steam. _____

10. What role does water vapor play in Earth's weather? _____

_____

_____

_____

11. What particles does air contain? _____

_____

_____

© Prentice-Hall, Inc.

● ●

SECTION 14–2 **Air Quality** (pages 446-449)

This section describes harmful substances in the air and explains how they can affect people and things. The section also describes what has been done to improve air quality.

▶ Air Pollution (pages 446–447)

1. Harmful substances in the air, water, or soil are known as

   _____.

2. How can air pollution affect human health? _____

   _____

   _____

   _____

3. Circle the letter of each sentence that is true about the causes of air pollution.

   a. Some air pollution occurs naturally.

   b. Much of air pollution is caused by human activities.

   c. Motor vehicles cause almost half the air pollution from human activities.

   d. Factories and power plants cause a little more than half of all air pollution.

▶ Particles (page 447)

4. What are some natural sources of particles in the atmosphere? _____

   _____

   _____

5. The average number of pollen grains in a cubic meter of air is known as

   the _____.

6. The particles in smoke that give it its dark color are _____.

CHAPTER 14, The Atmosphere *(continued)*

▶ Smog (page 448)

7. The brown haze that forms over sunny cities like Los Angeles is called

   _____.

8. Circle the letter of each sentence that is true about photochemical smog.

   a. It is caused by the action of sunlight on chemicals.

   b. It forms when particles in smoke combine with water droplets in air.

   c. It forms when nitrogen oxides and hydrocarbons react with each other.

   d. It is a mixture of ozone and other chemicals.

9. What effects does ozone have on people and things? _____

   _____

   _____

   _____

▶ Acid Rain (pages 448–449)

10. Is the following sentence true or false? One result of air pollution is

    acid rain. _____

11. Complete the flow chart.

Formation of Acid Rain

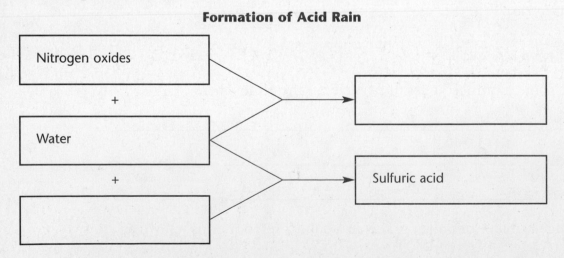

12. Is the following sentence true or false? Burning coal that is low in sulfur

    produces sulfur oxides. _____

© Prentice-Hall, Inc.

13. Rain that contains more acid than normal is known as

_____.

14. How can acid rain affect trees such as pines and spruce? _____

_____

_____

15. How can acid rain harm lakes and ponds? _____

_____

_____

_____

▶ **Improving Air Quality** (page 449)

16. What are some laws and regulations that have been passed to reduce air

pollution? _____

_____

_____

17. Is the following sentence true or false? Air quality in this country has

worsened over the past 30 years. _____

18. Is the following sentence true or false? The air in many American cities

is still polluted. _____

📖 **Reading Skill Practice**

When you read about a complex process, representing the process with a flowchart can help
you understand it. Make a flowchart to show how photochemical smog forms. For more
information on flowcharts, see page 721 of the Skills Handbook in your text. Do your work on a
separate sheet of paper.

CHAPTER 14, The Atmosphere *(continued)*

Air Pressure
(pages 451–456)

This section describes several properties of air, including density and air pressure. The section also explains how air pressure is measured and how it changes with altitude.

▶ **Properties of Air** (pages 451–452)

1. Circle the letter of each sentence that is true about air.

   a. Air has mass because it is composed of atoms and molecules.

   b. Because air has mass, it has density and pressure.

   c. The more molecules in a given volume of air, the greater its density.

   d. The greater the density of air, the less pressure it exerts.

2. Complete the table.

Properties of Air	
Property	**Definition**
	Amount of mass in a given volume of air
	Weight of the air pushing down on an area

3. Why doesn't air pressure crush your desk? _____

_____

_____

▶ **Measuring Air Pressure** (pages 452–453)

4. Is the following sentence true or false? Falling air pressure usually

   indicates that a storm is approaching. _____

5. An instrument that is used to measure changes in air pressure is a(n)

   _____.

6. Complete the concept map.

```
            ┌─────────────────┐
            │ Kinds of barometers │
            └─────────────────┘
                     │
                   include
          ╱                    ╲
   ┌──────────┐            ┌──────────┐
   │          │            │          │
   └──────────┘            └──────────┘
```

7. Is the following sentence true or false? The first barometers invented were aneroid barometers. _____

8. Draw a line on the glass tube to show where the level of the mercury might be if the air pressure fell.

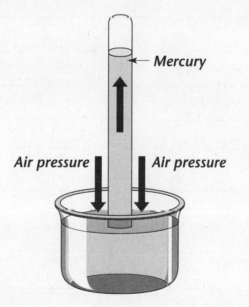

Mercury

Air pressure *Air pressure*

9. Why are aneroid barometers often more practical than mercury barometers? _____

_____

_____

10. Two different units used to measure air pressure are _____

and _____.

CHAPTER 14, The Atmosphere *(continued)*

11. If the air pressure is 30 inches, how many millibars of air pressure are

    there? _____

▶ **Increasing Altitude** (pages 454–456)

12. Another word for elevation, or distance above sea level, is

    _____.

13. Is the following sentence true or false? Air pressure increases as altitude

    increases. _____

14. Is the following sentence true or false? As air pressure decreases, so does

    air density. _____

15. Why is air pressure greatest at sea level? _____

    _____

    _____

    _____

16. Why is the air pressure on top of Mount McKinley less than the air

    pressure at sea level? _____

    _____

    _____

17. Is the following sentence true or false? As altitude increases, so does air

    density. _____

18. Circle the letter of the sentence that helps explain why you would have
    more difficulty breathing at high altitudes than at sea level.

    a. Air pressure is higher at high altitudes.

    b. Density of the air is greater at high altitudes.

    c. The percentage of oxygen in the air is lower at high altitudes.

    d. The amount of oxygen in each breath is less at high altitudes.

| SECTION 14–4 | **Layers of the Atmosphere** (pages 457–462) |

This section describes the four main layers of the atmosphere.

▶ Introduction (page 457)

1. The four main layers of the atmosphere are classified according to

   changes in _____.

2. Complete the concept map.

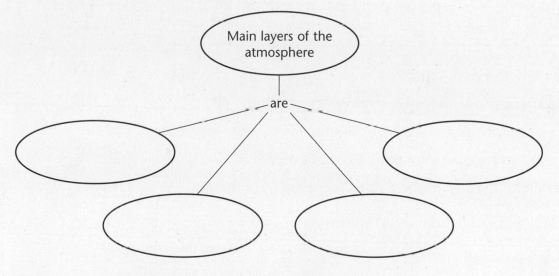

▶ The Troposphere (pages 457–458)

3. Circle the letter of each sentence that is true about the troposphere.
   a. It is the lowest layer of Earth's atmosphere.
   b. It has less variable conditions than other layers.
   c. It is where Earth's weather occurs.
   d. It is the shallowest layer of the atmosphere.

4. Is the following sentence true or false? The troposphere contains almost

   all of the mass of the atmosphere. _____

5. Is the following sentence true or false? As altitude increases in the

   troposphere, temperature also increases. _____

CHAPTER 14, The Atmosphere *(continued)*

6. How does the depth of the troposphere vary? _____

_____

_____

7. Is the following sentence true or false? At the top of the troposphere,

the temperature stays constant. _____

▶ The Stratosphere (page 458)

8. How far does the stratosphere extend above Earth's surface? _____

_____

9. Circle the letter of each sentence that is true about the stratosphere.

   a. The temperature of the lower stratosphere is about –60°C.

   b. The upper stratosphere is colder than the lower stratosphere.

   c. The upper stratosphere contains a layer of ozone.

   d. The ozone in the stratosphere reflects energy from the sun.

10. Why does a weather balloon keep increasing in volume as it rises

   through the stratosphere? _____

_____

_____

▶ The Mesosphere (pages 458–460)

11. Where does the mesosphere begin? _____

_____

12. Circle the letter of each sentence that is true about the mesosphere.

   a. It is the middle layer of the atmosphere.

   b. It contains the coldest part of the atmosphere.

   c. It protects Earth's surface from being hit by most meteoroids.

   d. It ends at 320 kilometers above sea level.

▶ **The Thermosphere** (pages 460–462)

13. Circle the letter of each sentence that is true about the thermosphere.

   a. It is the outermost layer of the atmosphere.

   b. Its air is very thin.

   c. It has no definite outer limit.

   d. It starts at 320 kilometers above sea level.

14. Why is the thermosphere so hot? _____

_____

_____

_____

15. Why would an ordinary thermometer show a low temperature in the

thermosphere? _____

_____

_____

_____

16. Complete the table.

Layers of the Thermosphere	
Layer	**Distance Above Sea Level**
	80–550 kilometers
	Above 550 kilometers

17. Brilliant light displays that occur in the ionosphere are called the

_____ .

18. Is the following sentence true or false? Satellites orbit Earth in the

exosphere. _____

CHAPTER 14, The Atmosphere *(continued)*

WordWise

Match each definition in the left column with the correct term in the right column. Then write the number of each term in the appropriate box below. When you have filled all the boxes, add up the numbers in each column, row, and two diagonals. All the sums should be the same.

Definitions

A. Mixture of gases that surrounds Earth

B. Form of oxygen with three atoms instead of two

C. Harmful substance in the air, water, or soil

D. Amount of mass in a given space

E. Amount of force pushing on an area

F. Elevation above sea level

G. Second-lowest layer of Earth's atmosphere

H. Outermost layer of Earth's atmosphere

I. Outer layer of the thermosphere

Terms

1. thermosphere

2. atmosphere

3. altitude

4. pollutant

5. pressure

6. stratosphere

7. density

8. exosphere

9. ozone

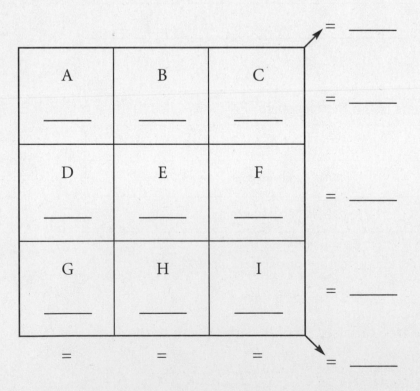

CHAPTER 15

WEATHER FACTORS

··

SECTION 15–1 **Energy in the Atmosphere** (pages 468–471)

This section explains how the atmosphere, or the air around Earth, is heated.

▶ **Energy from the Sun** (pages 468–469)

1. Is the following sentence true or false? About half the energy in Earth's

   atmosphere comes from the sun. _____

2. Energy from the sun travels to Earth as _____.

3. Is the following sentence true or false? Electromagnetic waves are
   classified according to wavelength, or the distance between waves.

   _____

4. The direct transfer of energy by electromagnetic waves is called

   _____.

Match the type of radiation with its description.

Type of Radiation	Description
_____ 5. visible light	**a.** It is a mixture of all the colors of the rainbow.
_____ 6. infrared radiation	**b.** It has wavelengths that are shorter than visible light.
_____ 7. ultraviolet radiation	**c.** It has wavelengths that are longer than visible light.

8. What causes the different colors of visible light? _____

   _____

   _____

CHAPTER 15, Weather Factors *(continued)*

9. Is the following sentence true or false? Red light has a shorter

wavelength than blue light. _____

10. Circle the letter of each sentence that is true about infrared radiation.

    a. It is invisible.   **b.** It can be felt as heat.

    c. It has longer wavelengths than red light.   **d.** It causes sunburn.

11. Circle the letter of each sentence that is true about ultraviolet radiation.

    a. It makes up most of the energy from the sun that reaches Earth.

    b. It can cause skin cancer and eye damage.

    c. It has longer wavelengths than violet light.

    d. It is used in heat lamps.

▶ Energy in the Atmosphere (pages 469–470)

12. Complete the concept map.

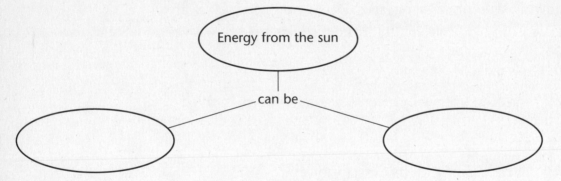

13. What absorbs or reflects energy from the sun in the atmosphere?

_____

_____

14. Reflection of light in all directions is called _____.

15. Circle the letter of each sentence that is true about scattering.

    a. Short wavelengths of visible light scatter less than long wavelengths.

    b. Blue light scatters less than red light.

    c. Scattered light is bluer than ordinary sunlight.

    d. Scattering explains why the daytime sky looks blue.

16. What happens to energy from the sun that is neither reflected nor

absorbed by the atmosphere? _____

_____

_____

▶ **Energy at Earth's Surface** (page 471)

17. Energy that is absorbed by the land and water is changed into

_____.

18. Is the following sentence true or false? When Earth's surface is heated, it
radiates some of the energy back into the atmosphere as ultraviolet

radiation. _____

19. What absorbs the energy that is radiated from Earth's surface?

_____

_____

20. The process by which gases hold heat in the air is called the

_____.

21. Is the following sentence true or false? The greenhouse effect is a

natural process. _____

SECTION 15-2 **Heat Transfer** (pages 474–477)

*This section explains what temperature measures and how temperature is related to
heat. The section also describes three ways that heat can be transferred from a hotter
object to a cooler one.*

▶ **Energy and Temperature** (pages 474–475)

1. Is the following sentence true or false? The faster the molecules of a gas

are moving, the more energy they have. _____

CHAPTER 15, Weather Factors *(continued)*

2. The total energy of motion in the molecules of a substance is called

   _____ .

3. The average amount of energy of motion of each molecule of a

   substance is called _____ .

4. Is the following sentence true or false? Temperature is a measure of how

   hot or cold a substance is. _____

▶ Measuring Temperature (page 475)

5. Air temperature is usually measured with a(n) _____ .

6. How does a thermometer work? _____

   _____

   _____

7. Complete the compare/contrast table.

Temperature Scales		
Scale	**Freezing Point of Water**	**Boiling Point of Water**
Celsius		
Fahrenheit		

▶ How Heat Is Transferred (pages 475–476)

8. The energy transferred from a hotter object to a cooler one is referred to

   as _____ .

9. Complete the concept map.

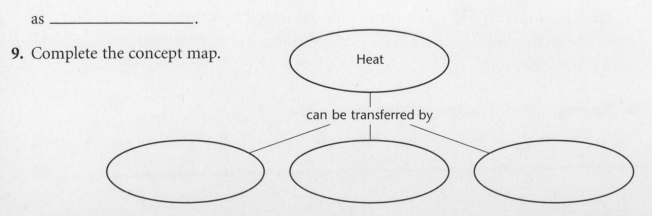

10. Is the following sentence true or false? Radiation is the direct transfer of energy by electromagnetic waves. _____

11. The direct transfer of heat from one substance to another substance that it is touching is called _____.

12. Circle the letter of each sentence that is true about conduction.

    a. It works well in some solids.   **b.** It works well in metals.

    c. It works best in liquids.   **d.** It works very well in air.

13. The transfer of heat by the movement of a fluid is called

    _____.

Match the type of heat transfer with its example.

Type of Heat Transfer   **Example**

_____ **14.** radiation   **a.** Drying your boots over a hot-air vent

_____ **15.** conduction   **b.** Burning your bare feet on hot sand

_____ **16.** convection   **c.** Feeling the sun's warmth on your face

▶ Heat Transfer in the Troposphere (pages 476–477)

17. In the drawing, label each of the ways that heat is transferred in the troposphere.

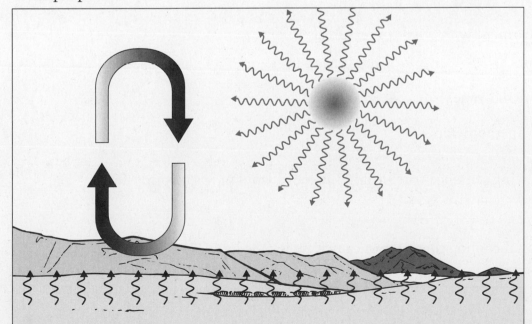

CHAPTER 15, Weather Factors *(continued)*

18. Most of the heating of the troposphere is caused by _____.

19. The upward movement of warm air and the downward movement of

cool air form _____.

• •

SECTION 15–3 Winds *(pages 478-486)*

This section explains what causes winds and how winds are measured. The section also describes different types of winds that blow across Earth's surface.

▶ What Causes Winds? (pages 478–479)

1. The horizontal movement of air from an area of high pressure to an

area of lower pressure is referred to as _____.

2. Is the following sentence true or false? All winds are caused by

differences in air pressure. _____

3. What is the ultimate source of energy that powers the wind? _____

_____

▶ Measuring Wind (page 479)

Match the instrument with what it measures.

Instrument	What It Measures
_____ **4.** wind vane	**a.** wind speed
_____ **5.** anemometer	**b.** wind direction

6. Is the following sentence true or false? A south wind blows toward the

south. _____

7. The increased cooling that a wind can cause is called the

_____.

Science Explorer *Focus on Earth Science*

8. Why does the wind blowing over your skin make you feel colder?

_____

_____

▶ Local Winds (pages 480–482)

9. Winds that blow over short distances are called _____.

10. What causes local winds? _____

_____

11. Circle the letter of each sentence that is true about the unequal heating of land and water.

    a. Land warms up faster than water.

    b. During the day, air over water is warmer than air over land.

    c. Water cools more quickly than land.

    d. At night, air over water is cooler than air over land.

12. Label the drawings to indicate which drawing shows a sea breeze and which drawing shows a land breeze.

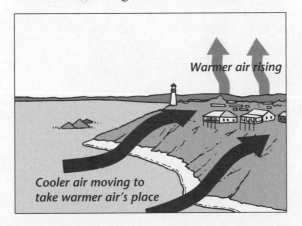

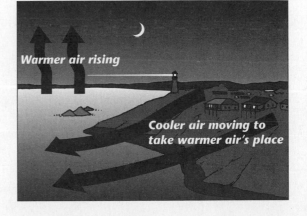

_____   _____

▶ Monsoons (page 482)

13. Circle the letter of each sentence that is true about monsoons.

    a. They are caused by unequal heating of land and water.

    b. They occur in the South Atlantic.

    c. They always blow in the same direction.

    d. They supply the rains needed by crops.

CHAPTER 15, Weather Factors (continued)

▶ Global Winds (page 483)

14. Winds that blow steadily from specific directions over long distances

    are called _____.

15. Circle the letter of each sentence that is true about global winds.

    a. They are created by unequal heating of Earth's surface.

    b. They are produced by the movement of air between the equator and the poles.

    c. They blow in a straight line from the poles toward the equator.

    d. They curve because of Earth's rotation.

16. As Earth rotates, the Coriolis effect causes winds in the Northern

    Hemisphere to turn toward the _____.

▶ Global Wind Belts (pages 484–486)

17. The calm areas around Earth include the _____ and the

    _____.

18. Complete the compare/contrast table.

Directions of Global Wind Belts	
Wind Belt	**Direction It Blows**
	Toward the equator
	Toward the poles
	Away from the poles

▶ Jet Streams (page 486)

19. Circle the letter of each sentence that is true about jet streams.

    a. They are about 100 kilometers above Earth's surface.

    b. They are hundreds of kilometers wide.

    c. They blow from east to west.

    d. They blow at speeds of 200 to 400 kilometers per hour.

Science Explorer *Focus on Earth Science*

SECTION 15-4 Water in the Atmosphere (pages 487-492)

This section explains what humidity is and how it is measured. The section also explains how clouds form and describes different types of clouds.

▶ Introduction (page 487)

1. The process by which water molecules in liquid water escape into the air

   as water vapor is called _____.

2. What is the water cycle? _____

   _____

▶ Humidity (page 488)

3. A measure of the amount of water vapor in the air is _____.

4. What is relative humidity? _____

   _____

   _____

5. Circle the letter of each sentence that is true about relative humidity.

   a. It is a percentage.

   b. It is all the water vapor the air can hold.

   c. It depends on air temperature.

   d. It measures how hot it feels.

6. How does evaporation of moisture from your skin help keep you

   comfortable on a hot day? _____

   _____

   _____

▶ Measuring Relative Humidity (pages 488–489)

7. Relative humidity can be measured with a(n) _____.

CHAPTER 15, Weather Factors *(continued)*

8. Circle the letter of each sentence that is true about how a psychrometer works.

   a. The dry-bulb thermometer is cooled by evaporation when the wind blows.

   b. The higher the humidity, the faster water evaporates from the bulb.

   c. The wet-bulb thermometer reading is always higher than the dry-bulb reading.

   d. When relative humidity is high, there is not much difference between thermometer readings.

▶ How Clouds Form (pages 489–490)

9. Is the following sentence true or false? Clouds form when water vapor

   in the air becomes liquid water or ice crystals. _____

Match the term with its definition.

Term	Definition
_____ 10. condensation	**a.** Ice that has been deposited directly from the air onto a cold surface
_____ 11. dew point	**b.** Water that condenses from the air onto a cold surface
_____ 12. dew	**c.** Temperature at which condensation begins
_____ 13. frost	**d.** Process by which molecules of water vapor become liquid water

14. Circle the letter of each sentence that is true about condensation of water vapor.

   a. It occurs when air gets warmer.   **b.** It can occur on cold surfaces.

   c. It is why clouds form.   **d.** It occurs when air sinks.

15. What causes the clouds to form on the windward side of the mountain?

   _____

   _____

▶ **Types of Clouds** (pages 490–492)

Match the type of cloud with its height.

Type of Cloud

_____ **16.** cumulus

_____ **17.** stratus

_____ **18.** cirrus

_____ **19.** fog

Height

a. About 2 to 18 kilometers above the surface

b. More than 6 kilometers above the surface

c. At or near the surface

d. 2 to 6 kilometers above the surface

20. Complete the table.

Types of Clouds	
Type of Cloud	**Description**
	Looks like fluffy piles of cotton
	Forms in flat layers
	Looks wispy and feathery

21. Circle the letter of each sentence that is true about cloud types.

a. Cumulus clouds are usually a sign that a storm is approaching.

b. Cumulonimbus and nimbostratus clouds produce rain or snow.

c. Altostratus clouds are lower than regular stratus clouds.

d. Cirrus clouds are made up mostly of ice crystals.

Reading Skill Practice

When you read a section with a lot of details, writing an outline can help you organize and remember the material. Outline Section 15-4 by first writing the section headings as major topics in the order in which they appear in the book. Then, beneath each major topic, list important details about it. Title your outline *Water in the Atmosphere.* Do your work on a separate sheet of paper.

CHAPTER 15, Weather Factors (*continued*)

SECTION 15-5
Precipitation
(pages 493-496)

This section explains how rain, snow, and other common types of precipitation occur and how they are measured. The section also describes how scientists try to produce rain from clouds.

▶ **Introduction** (page 493)

1. What is precipitation? _____

_____

_____

2. Is the following sentence true or false? All clouds produce precipitation.

_____

▶ **Types of Precipitation** (pages 493–495)

3. Complete the compare/contrast table.

Types of Precipitation	
Type of Precipitation	**Description**
	Drops of water at least 0.5 mm in diameter
	Ice particles smaller than 5 mm in diameter
	Ice pellets larger than 5 mm in diameter
	Ice crystals

4. Is the following sentence true or false? The most common kind of

precipitation is snow. _____

5. How do mist and drizzle differ from rain? _____

_____

_____

Science Explorer *Focus on Earth Science*

6. Why do ice storms cause power failures? _____

_____

_____

Match the type of precipitation with how it forms

Type of Precipitation	How It Forms

_____ **7.** sleet

_____ **8.** freezing rain

_____ **9.** hail

_____ **10.** snow

a. Water vapor in a cloud is converted directly into ice crystals.

b. Ice pellets add layers of ice as they are carried up and down in a storm cloud.

c. Raindrops freeze after they hit the ground and other surfaces.

d. Raindrops freeze into tiny particles of ice as they fall through the air.

11. What damage can large hailstones do? _____

_____

_____

▶ Measuring Precipitation (page 495)

12. Meteorologists measure rainfall with a(n) _____.

13. Is the following sentence true or false? On average, 10 centimeters of snow contains about the same amount of water as 5 centimeters of rain. _____

▶ Controlling Precipitation (page 496)

14. Long periods of unusually low precipitation are called _____.

15. Circle the letter of each sentence that is true about cloud seeding.

    a. It is the most common way to produce rain from clouds.

    b. It adds water vapor to the air so clouds will form.

    c. It adds particles to clouds so water vapor can condense.

    d. It has been used to clear fog from airports.

© Prentice-Hall, Inc.

CHAPTER 15, Weather Factors (continued)

WordWise

Test your knowledge of key terms from Chapter 15 by solving the crossword puzzle.

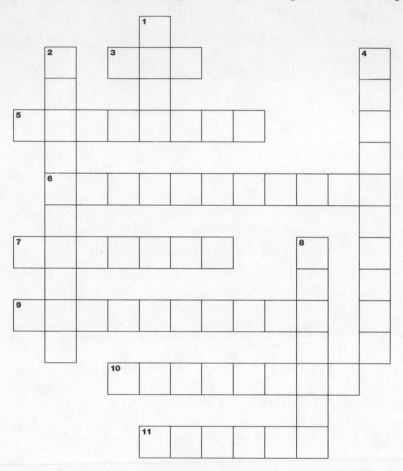

Clues down

1. The energy transferred from a hotter object to a cooler one

2. Reflection of light in all directions

4. Transfer of heat by movements of a fluid

8. Clouds that form in flat layers

Clues across

3. Type of breeze that blows from an ocean or lake to the land

5. Distance north or south from the equator measured in degrees

6. Average amount of energy of motion in the molecules of a substance

7. Water shortage caused by long periods of low precipitation

9. Instrument used to measure wind speed

10. Measure of the amount of water vapor in the air

11. Clouds made mostly of ice crystals that form high above Earth

CHAPTER 16

WEATHER PATTERNS

. . . .

SECTION 16-1 Air Masses and Fronts
(pages 502-508)

This section describes huge bodies of air, called air masses, and explains how they move. The section also explains how the meeting of different air masses affects weather.

▶ **Introduction** (page 502)

1. What is an air mass? _____

_____

_____

▶ **Types of Air Masses** (pages 502–504)

2. Scientists classify air masses according to _____ and

_____.

3. Is the following sentence true or false? Polar air masses have low air

pressure. _____

4. Complete the compare/contrast table.

Types of Air Masses and Their Characteristics	
Type of Air Mass	**Characteristics**
	Warm and humid
	Cool and humid
	Warm and dry
	Cool and dry

CHAPTER 16, Weather Patterns *(continued)*

▶ How Air Masses Move (page 505)

5. In the continental United States, major wind belts generally push air

   masses from _____ to _____.

▶ Fronts (pages 505–507)

6. Label the drawings to indicate a cold front and a warm front.

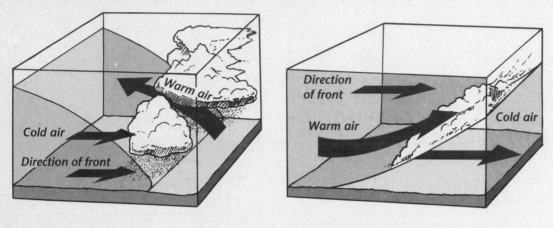

_____   _____

Match the type of front with how it forms.

Type of Front

_____ 7. cold front

_____ 8. warm front

_____ 9. stationary front

_____ 10. occluded front

How It Forms

a. A moving warm air mass collides with a slowly moving cold air mass.

b. A warm air mass is caught between two cooler air masses.

c. A rapidly moving cold air mass runs into a slowly moving warm air mass.

d. A cold air mass and a warm air mass meet and remain stalled over an area.

11. Circle the letter of each sentence that is true about fronts.

    a. Cold fronts can cause violent thunderstorms.

    b. Warm fronts are associated with clouds and rain.

    c. Stationary fronts may bring many days of clouds and precipitation.

    d. Occluded fronts always bring fair weather.

▶ Cyclones and Anticyclones (pages 507–508)

12. A swirling center of low air pressure is called a(n) _____.

13. Is the following sentence true or false? Winds spiral inward toward the

center of a cyclone. _____

14. What type of weather is associated with cyclones? _____

_____

_____

15. Is the following sentence true or false? Winds in an anticyclone spin

clockwise in the Northern Hemisphere. _____

16. What type of weather is associated with anticyclones? _____

_____

_____

Storms (pages 509–517)

SECTION 16–2

*This section explains how thunderstorms, tornadoes, hurricanes, and snow storms form.
The section also describes how people can stay safe in the different types of storms.*

▶ Introduction (page 509)

1. What is a storm? _____

_____

▶ Thunderstorms (pages 510–511)

2. Circle the letter of the type of clouds in which thunderstorms form.

a. cumulus **b.** nimbus

c. nimbostratus **d.** cumulonimbus

3. A sudden energy discharge between parts of a cloud or between the

cloud and the ground is called _____.

CHAPTER 16, Weather Patterns *(continued)*

4. Circle the letter of each sentence that is true about thunder.

    a. It is the sound of an explosion.

    b. It occurs after lightning.

    c. It occurs because lightning heats the air.

    d. It occurs because light travels faster than sound.

5. Circle the letter of each sentence that is a way to stay safe in a thunderstorm.

    a. Avoid touching metal objects.

    b. Get out of the water.

    c. Don't use the telephone.

    d. Get out of your car and go under a tree.

▶ Tornadoes (pages 511–514)

6. What is a tornado? _____

_____

_____

7. Is the following sentence true or false? Tornadoes develop in the same

clouds that bring thunderstorms. _____

8. Circle the letter of each sentence that is true about where and when tornadoes occur.

    a. Tornadoes are most likely in late summer and early fall.

    b. Tornadoes occur often in the Great Plains.

    c. Tornadoes occur more often in the United States than in any other country.

    d. Tornadoes occur in just a few parts of the United States.

9. Where is the safest place to be during a tornado? _____

_____

_____

▶ Hurricanes (pages 514–516)

10. Circle the letter of each sentence that is true about a hurricane.

    a. It is a tropical storm.

    b. It has winds of at least 159 kilometers per hour.

    c. It is typically about 60 kilometers across.

    d. It forms over water.

11. The quiet center of a hurricane is called the _____.

12. Is the following sentence true or false? Hurricanes do not last as long as

other storms. _____

13. A "dome" of water that sweeps across the coast where the hurricane

lands is called a(n) _____.

14. Is the following sentence true or false? If you hear a hurricane warning
and are told to evacuate, you should leave the area immediately.

_____

▶ Winter Storms (pages 516–517)

15. When does snow fall? _____

_____

16. Circle the letter of each sentence that is true about lake-effect snow.

    a. It occurs in Detroit and Chicago.

    b. It occurs because land cools more rapidly than water.

    c. It occurs on the south and west sides of the Great Lakes.

    d. It occurs when humid air rises and cools over land.

17. What should you do if you are caught in a snowstorm? _____

_____

_____

_____

_____

CHAPTER 16, Weather Patterns *(continued)*

 **Floods**
16-3 (pages 521-524)

This section explains why floods occur and describes how to stay safe in floods.

▶ **Flash Floods** (page 522)

1. Is the following sentence true or false? Floods are the most dangerous

   weather-related events in the United States. _____

2. A sudden, violent flood that occurs within a few hours, or even minutes,

   of a storm is called a(n) _____.

3. Complete the concept map.

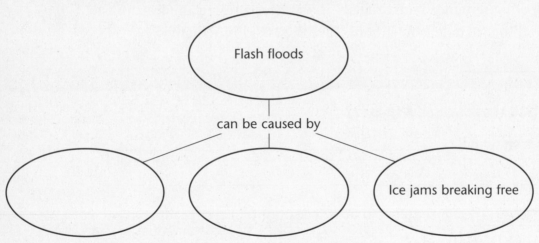

▶ **Flood Safety Measures** (pages 522–524)

4. Why do scientists try to predict floods? _____

   _____

   _____

5. An announcement describing the area in which flooding is possible is

   a(n) _____.

6. An announcement that floods have already been reported or are about

   to occur is a(n) _____.

7. What is the first rule of flood safety? _____

_____

_____

8. Circle the letter of each choice that is a flood hazard.

    a. power outages

    b. landslides

    c. polluted drinking water

    d. interruption of emergency services

Reading Skill Practice

As you read, identifying the sentence that best expresses the main topic under each heading can help you focus on the most important points. For each heading in Section 16-3, identify and copy the sentence that best expresses the main topic under that heading. Do your work on a separate sheet of paper.

SECTION 16–4 **Predicting the Weather** (pages 525-531)

This section explains how scientists predict the weather in the future and why it is difficult to predict the weather accurately. The section also explains how to read weather maps.

▶ Weather Forecasting (page 526)

1. Scientists who study the causes of weather and try to predict it are called

    _____.

2. Meteorologists get weather information from which of the following sources?

    a. radar   **b.** seismographs

    c. instruments carried by balloons   **d.** satellites

CHAPTER 16, Weather Patterns *(continued)*

▶ Weather Technology *(page 527)*

3. In what two areas have changes in technology occurred in weather

forecasting? _____

_____

4. Is the following sentence true or false? Weather forecasts for over three

days into the future are never reliable. _____

5. Circle the letter of each sentence that is true about weather balloons or weather satellites.

   a. Weather balloons carry instruments into the stratosphere.

   b. Weather balloons carry computers to analyze weather data.

   c. The first weather satellite was launched in 1940.

   d. Weather satellites take pictures of Earth from the exosphere.

6. Circle the letter of each sentence that is true about computer forecasts of the weather.

   a. Computers are rarely used to help forecast weather.

   b. Computer forecasts are based on weather conditions from many weather stations.

   c. Computers only make long-term forecasts of a week or more.

   d. When new weather data come in, computers revise their forecasts.

▶ El Niño *(page 528)*

7. A warm-water event that occurs periodically in the Pacific Ocean is

called _____.

8. Circle the letter of each sentence that is true about El Niño.

   a. When it occurs, warm surface water is pushed toward South America.

   b. It prevents cold water from rising to the surface near the coast of South America.

   c. It occurs once every five to ten years.

   d. It can affect weather patterns in places as far away as Florida.

▶ Reading Weather Maps (pages 528–530)

9. What data are shown on a weather map? _____

_____

_____

_____

_____

10. What are the temperature, air pressure, and wind direction at the weather station represented by the symbol shown here? _____

_____

_____

38 ● 1018

Match the term with its definition.

Term	Definition
_____ **11.** isobars	**a.** Lines on a weather map joining places that have the same temperature
_____ **12.** isotherms	**b.** Lines on a weather map joining places that have the same air pressure

▶ The Butterfly Effect (pages 530–531)

13. Why is weather forecasting tricky, even with current technology?

_____

_____

_____

14. Is the following sentence true or false? The butterfly effect refers to the fact that a small change in the weather today can mean a larger change in the weather a week later. _____

CHAPTER 16, Weather Patterns (continued)

WordWise

Solve the clues by filling in the blanks with key terms from Chapter 16. Then write the numbered letters in the correct order to find the hidden message.

Clues	Key Terms
Violent disturbance in the atmosphere	_ _ _ _ _ 1 2
Type of air mass that forms north of 50° north latitude or south of 50° south latitude	_ _ _ _ _ 3 4
Type of air mass that forms over oceans	_ _ _ _ _ _ _ 5
Lines on a map joining places that have the same air pressure	_ _ _ _ _ _ _ 6 7 8
Type of front in which a warm air mass is cut off from the ground by cool air beneath it	_ _ _ _ _ _ _ _ 9 10
Type of air mass that forms in the tropics	_ _ _ _ _ _ _ _ 11
A sudden spark when electrical charges jump between parts of a cloud or between a cloud and the ground	_ _ _ _ _ _ _ _ _ 12 13
Lines on a map joining places that have the same temperature	_ _ _ _ _ _ _ 14 15
Rapidly whirling, funnel-shaped cloud that reaches down from a storm cloud to touch Earth's surface	_ _ _ _ _ _ 16
Tropical storm with winds of 119 kilometers per hour or higher	_ _ _ _ _ _ _ _ 17
Scientist who studies the causes of weather and tries to predict it	_ _ _ _ _ _ _ _ _ _ _ _ 18

Hidden Message

$\overline{}$ $\overline{}$ $\overline{}$ $\overline{}$ $\overline{}$ $\overline{}$ $\overline{}$ $\overline{}$ $\overline{}$ $\overline{}$ $\overline{}$ $\overline{}$ $\overline{}$ $\overline{}$ $\overline{}$ $\overline{}$ $\overline{}$ $\overline{}$.
1   2   3   4   5   6   7   8   9   10   11   12   13   14   15   16   17   18

CHAPTER 17

CLIMATE AND CLIMATE CHANGE

• •

SECTION 17–1 **What Causes Climate?**
(pages 538–545)

This section describes factors that determine climate, or the average weather conditions in an area. The section also explains what causes the seasons.

▶ Introduction (page 538)

1. The average, year-after-year conditions of temperature, precipitation,

   winds, and clouds in an area is the _____.

2. Complete the concept map.

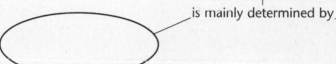

▶ Factors Affecting Temperature (pages 539–541)

3. What are the main factors that influence temperature? _____

   _____

   _____

4. It is colder at high latitudes because the sun's rays strike Earth's surface

   at a _____ angle there.

5. List the three temperature zones on Earth's surface that are based on
   latitude.

   a. _____ b. _____ c. _____

CHAPTER 17, Climate and Climate Change *(continued)*

6. Is the following sentence true or false? Areas at high altitudes have cool climates no matter what their latitude. _____

Match the type of climate with its description.

Type of Climate

_____ **7.** marine climate

_____ **8.** continental climate

Description

a. Relatively warm winters and cool summers

b. Cold winters and warm or hot summers

9. Circle the letter of each sentence that is true about how ocean currents influence climates.

    a. Ocean currents influence many marine climates.

    b. Only warm ocean currents influence climates.

    c. The North Atlantic Drift gives Ireland a warm climate for its latitude.

    d. The California Current gives the West Coast a warm climate for its latitude.

▶ Factors Affecting Precipitation (pages 542–543)

10. List the main factors that affect precipitation.

    a. _____   **b.** _____

11. Why does precipitation occur when warm air rises? _____

_____

_____

12. Circle the letter of each sentence that is true about the effect of mountain ranges on precipitation.

    a. Precipitation falls on the leeward side of mountains.

    b. The windward side of mountains is in a rain shadow.

    c. Air that flows over the mountains loses a lot of water vapor as it rises.

    d. Precipitation falls on the side of the mountains that the oncoming wind hits.

13. Is the following sentence true or false? Winds blowing inland from oceans

carry less water than winds blowing from land. _____

▶ Microclimates (page 543)

14. The climate characteristic of a small specific area is a(n)

_____.

15. What are some natural features than can result in a microclimate?

_____

_____

_____

▶ The Seasons (pages 544–545)

16. Is the following sentence true or false? It is colder in the winter in the
Northern Hemisphere because Earth is farther from the sun then.

_____

17. When Earth is in the position shown in the drawing, what season is it

in the Northern Hemisphere? _____

_____

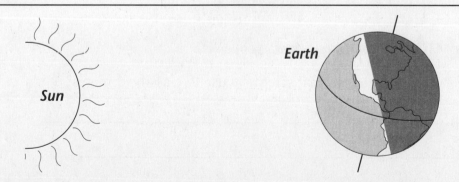

18. Circle the letter of each sentence that is true about Earth's axis.

a. The axis always points in the same direction.

b. The north end of the axis is tilted away from the sun all year.

c. When it is summer in the Southern Hemisphere, the south end of
the axis is tilted toward the sun.

d. In March and November, neither end of the axis is tilted toward the sun.

CHAPTER 17, Climate and Climate Change *(continued)*

19. Why is Earth's surface warmer in the Northern Hemisphere when it is

summer there? _____

_____

_____

📖 Reading Skill Practice

When you read a section with difficult material, turning the headings into questions and then trying to find the answers can help you focus on the most important points. For each heading in Section 17-1, first turn the heading into a question, and then try to find the answer. Do your work on a separate sheet of paper.

SECTION 17-2 **Climate Regions** (pages 548-557)

This section explains how scientists classify climates and describes five major climate regions.

▶ Classifying Climates (pages 548–549)

1. What are the two major factors that scientists use to classify climates?

_____

_____

2. List the five major climate regions.

a. _____ b. _____ c. _____

d. _____ e. _____

3. Is the following sentence true or false? A highland climate can occur

within any of the other climate regions. _____

▶ Tropical Rainy Climates (pages 549–552)

4. Complete the concept map.

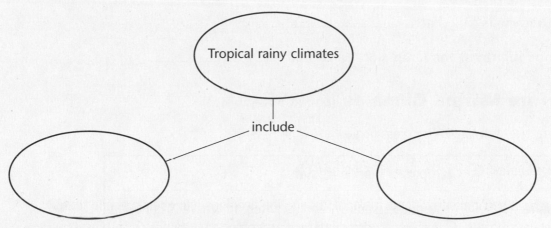

5. Circle the letter of each sentence that is true about a tropical wet climate.

   a. It has heavy rainfall year round.

   b. It is hot year-round.

   c. Rain forests grow in this type of climate.

   d. Florida has this type of climate.

6. Circle the letter of each sentence that is true about a tropical wet-and-dry climate.

   a. It has a wet season and a dry season.

   b. It is hot year-round.

   c. Grasslands grow in this type of climate.

   d. Hawaii has this type of climate.

▶ Dry Climates (pages 552–553)

7. Arid regions, which get less than 25 centimeters of rain every year, are

   also called _____.

8. Where are there arid climates in the United States? _____

   _____

   _____

CHAPTER 17, Climate and Climate Change *(continued)*

9. An area that is dry but gets enough rainfall for short grasses and low

bushes to grow is called a(n) _____.

10. The steppe region of the United States is the _____.

▶ Temperate Marine Climates (pages 553–554)

11. Complete the compare/contrast table.

Temperate Marine Climates		
Type of Climate	**Characteristics**	**Region Where It Is Found**
	Cool and wet	Pacific Northwest
	Warm and dry	Southern coast of California
	Warm and wet	Southeastern United States

▶ Temperate Continental Climates (page 555)

12. Circle the letter of each sentence that is true about temperate
continental climates.

    a. They are found in both Northern and Southern hemispheres.

    b. They are greatly influenced by oceans.

    c. They have extremes of temperature.

    d. They are found in the northeastern United States.

13. Is the following sentence true or false? Humid continental climates

receive less precipitation in summer than in winter. _____

14. What are summers and winters like in subarctic climates? _____

_____

▶ Polar Climates (page 556)

15. Is the following sentence true or false? The polar climate is the coldest

climate region. _____

© Prentice-Hall, Inc.

16. Complete the compare/contrast table.

Polar Climates		
Type of Climate	**Warmest Temperature**	**Organisms Found There**
	0° C (freezing)	Only lichens and a few low plants
Tundra		Many kinds of plants and animals

▶ Highlands (page 557)

17. How do highland climates differ from climates of the regions that

surround them? _____

_____

_____

18. The climate above the tree line is like that of the _____.

· ·

SECTION 17-3 Long-Term Changes in Climate
(pages 560-564)

This section explains how scientists learn about past climates and describes a time in the past when ice covered large parts of Earth. The section also gives some possible reasons why climates have changed

▶ Studying Climate Change (page 561)

1. Circle the letter of each choice that provides evidence of ancient climates.

    a. fossils   **b.** tree rings   **c.** pollen records   **d.** weather maps

2. Why do scientists think that Greenland's climate was warm and moist

80 million years ago? _____

_____

_____

_____

CHAPTER 17, Climate and Climate Change *(continued)*

3. Is the following sentence true or false? A thin tree ring indicates that the

year was warm or wet. _____

▶ **Ice Ages** (page 562)

4. Circle the letter of the sentence that is true about the ice ages.

a. When they occurred, glaciers covered all of Earth's surface.

b. There have been at least six major ice ages in the past two million years.

c. Each of the major ice ages lasted 100,000 years or longer.

d. The most recent major ice age ended about 105,000 years ago.

5. Is the following sentence true or false? Some scientists think that we are

now in a warm period between ice ages. _____

6. Why was the sea level lower during the ice ages? _____

_____

_____

▶ **Causes of Climate Change** (pages 563–564)

7. Complete the concept map.

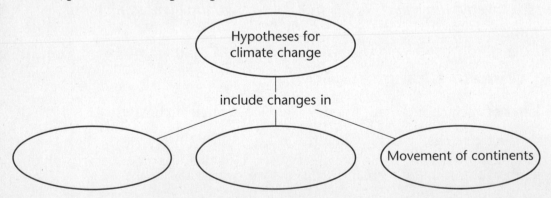

8. What changes in Earth's position may have affected climates? _____

_____

_____

_____

9. Circle the letter of each sentence that is true about sunspots.

   a. They are dark, cooler regions on the surface of the sun.

   b. They increase and decrease in 100-year cycles.

   c. They could be caused by changes in the sun's energy output.

   d. They are known to be the chief cause of the ice ages.

10. Circle the letter of each sentence that is true about the movement of Earth's continents.

   a. Earth's continents have always been located where they are now.

   b. Most of the land on Earth was once part of a single continent.

   c. Continents now near the poles were once near the equator.

   d. The movement of continents has had no effect on climates.

• •

SECTION 17-4 **Global Changes in the Atmosphere** (pages 565-568)

This section explains how human activities may be increasing Earth's temperature by changing the atmosphere.

▶ **Global Warming** (pages 565–567)

1. Is the following sentence true or false? Over the last 120 years, the average temperature of the troposphere has risen by about 5° C.

   _____

Match the term with its definition.

Term	Definition
_____ 2. greenhouse effect	a. Process by which Earth's atmosphere traps solar energy
_____ 3. global warming	b. Gradual increase in the temperature of Earth's atmosphere

4. Gases in the atmosphere that trap solar energy are called

   _____ .

CHAPTER 17, Climate and Climate Change *(continued)*

5. What are some greenhouse gases? _____

_____

_____

6. How may human activities be warming Earth's atmosphere? _____

_____

_____

_____

7. Circle the letter of the choice that is the outcome of burning wood, coal, oil, and natural gas.

   a. Carbon dioxide is added to the air.

   b. Global warming is prevented.

   c. Less heat is trapped by Earth's atmosphere.

   d. The amount of carbon dioxide in the air decreases.

8. Is the following sentence true or false? The amount of carbon dioxide in the air has been steadily increasing. _____

9. Is the following sentence true or false? Everyone agrees about the causes of global warming. _____

10. How might changes in solar energy affect Earth's climate? _____

_____

_____

11. Circle the letter of each choice that is a possible effect of global warming.

   a. Places too warm for farming today could become farmland.

   b. Fertile fields might become "dust bowls."

   c. The number of hurricanes might decrease.

   d. Low-lying coastal areas might be flooded.

▶ Ozone Depletion (pages 567–568)

12. Is the following sentence true or false? Ozone in the stratosphere filters out much of the harmful ultraviolet radiation from the sun.

_____

13. Is the following sentence true or false? The ozone layer over Antarctica is growing thinner. _____

14. What are chlorofluorocarbons, or CFCs? _____

_____

_____

15. Complete the flowchart.

CFCs and Ozone Depletion

CFCs are released into air.

↓

↓

CFCs break down into chlorine atoms.

↓

16. With a decrease in ozone, the amount of ultraviolet radiation reaching Earth's surface would _____ .

17. What have the United States and other countries done to try to prevent ozone depletion? _____

_____

_____

CHAPTER 17, Climate and Climate Change *(continued)*

WordWise

Use the clues to help you unscramble the key terms from Chapter 17. Then put the numbered letters in order to find the answer to the riddle.

Clues   **Key Terms**

Climate characteristic of a small, specific area   _ _ _ _ _ _ _ _ _ _ _ _ _
                                                         1

Downwind side of mountains   _ _ _ _ _ _ _
                                                    2

Average conditions of temperature,   _ _ _ _ _ _ _
precipitation, winds, and clouds in an area   3

Permanently frozen soil found in the tundra   _ _ _ _ _ _ _ _ _ _
climate region   4

Tropical grassland found in the tropical wet-   _ _ _ _ _ _ _
and-dry climate   5

Polar climate region with short, cool summers   _ _ _ _ _ _
and bitterly cold winters   6

Region that receives less than 25 centimeters   _ _ _ _ _ _
of rain a year   7

Riddle: What is determined by temperature and precipitation?

Answer: _ _ _ _ _ _ _
            1 2 3 4 5 6 7

Science Explorer *Focus on Earth Science*

CHAPTER 18

POPULATIONS AND COMMUNITIES

· ·

SECTION 18–1 Living Things and the Environment (pages 578-583)

This section describes what organisms need and how their environments provide for their needs. The section also describes how organisms live together in populations and communities.

▶ Introduction (pages 578–579)

1. All the living and nonliving things that interact in a particular area make

   up a(n) _____.

▶ Habitats (page 579)

2. The place where an organism lives and that provides the things the

   organism needs is called its _____.

3. What needs of an organism are provided by its habitat? _____

   _____

4. Is the following sentence true or false? Each ecosystem contains one

   habitat. _____

▶ Biotic Factors (page 579)

5. Circle the letter of each choice that is a biotic factor in a prairie dog
   ecosystem.

   a. Grass and other plants that the prairie dog eats

   b. Hawks, ferrets, and other animals that hunt the prairie dog

   c. The soil that provides the prairie dog with a home

   d. Worms, fungi, and bacteria that also live in the soil

CHAPTER 18, Populations and Communities *(continued)*

6. The living parts of an ecosystem are called _____.

▶ Abiotic Factors (pages 580–581)

7. The nonliving parts of an ecosystem are called _____.

8. Complete the concept map.

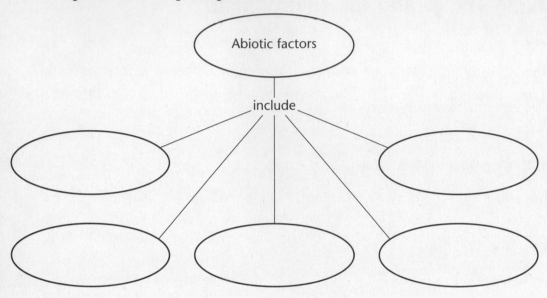

9. Circle the letter of each sentence that is true about water.

   a. It is needed by all living things.

   b. It makes up 95 percent of the human body.

   c. It is needed by algae and plants to make food.

   d. It is an abiotic factor only for organisms that actually live in the water.

10. The process in which plants and algae make food using water, sunlight,

   and carbon dioxide is called _____.

11. Circle the letter of each sentence that is true about oxygen.

   a. Humans can live only a few hours without it.

   b. Organisms that live on land get it from the air.

   c. It makes up about 40 percent of air.

   d. Fish get it from the water around them.

Science Explorer *Focus on Earth Science*

▶ Populations (page 581)

12. What is a species? _____

_____

_____

13. Circle the letter of each choice that is an example of a population.

   a. All the prairie dogs in a prairie dog town

   b. All the daisies in a field

   c. All the pigeons in New York City

   d. All the trees in a forest

14. Is the following sentence true or false? All populations live in the same-sized area. _____

▶ Communities (page 582)

15. All the different populations that live together in an area make up a(n)

_____.

16. Circle the letter of the choice that lists the levels of organization in an ecosystem from the smallest unit of organization to the largest.

   a. Population, organism, community, ecosystem

   b. Organism, population, ecosystem, community

   c. Organism, community, population, ecosystem

   d. Organism, population, community, ecosystem

17. In addition to a community of different species, what else does an

ecosystem include? _____

_____

18. Is the following sentence true or false? To be considered a community, populations must live close enough together to interact. _____

CHAPTER 18, Populations and Communities *(continued)*

▶ What Is Ecology? (pages 582–583)

19. What is ecology? _____

_____

_____

20. Scientists who study how living things interact with each other and

with their environment are called _____.

· ·

SECTION 18-2 Studying Populations (pages 585–590)

This section describes how scientists study population density, size, and growth. The section also explains how factors such as food, space, and weather limit how large populations can become.

▶ Population Density (page 585)

1. Is the following sentence true or false? Population density is the

number of individuals in a specific area. _____

▶ Determining Population Size (pages 586–587)

Match the type of study with its example.

Type of Study	Example
_____ **2.** direct observation	**a.** Counting the number of nesting sites in an area
_____ **3.** indirect observation	**b.** Counting all the bald eagles that live along a river
_____ **4.** sampling	**c.** Counting hawks with and without bands on their legs
_____ **5.** mark-and-recapture study	**d.** Counting the number of red maples in a small area to estimate the number in the entire forest

▶ Changes in Population Size (pages 587–588)

6. How can populations change in size? _____

_____

_____

7. What is the major way in which new individuals are added to a

population? _____

_____

8. The number of births in a population in a certain amount of time is

the _____.

9. What is the major way that individuals leave a population? _____

_____

10. The number of deaths in a population in a certain amount of time is

the _____.

11. Is the following sentence true or false? If the birth rate is greater than

the death rate, population size decreases. _____

Match the term with its definition

Term	Definition
_____ **12.** immigration	**a.** Leaving a population
_____ **13.** emigration	**b.** Moving into a population

▶ Limiting Factors (pages 589–590)

14. An environmental factor that prevents a population from increasing is

called a(n) _____.

15. What are some limiting factors for populations? _____

_____

_____

CHAPTER 18, Populations and Communities *(continued)*

16. The largest population that an environment can support is called its

_____.

17. Is the following sentence true or false? Space is often a limiting factor

for plants. _____

18. What are some ways weather conditions can limit population growth?

_____

_____

• •

SECTION 18-3

Interactions Among Living Things
(pages 593-600)

This section explains how organisms become adapted to their environments. The section also describes three major types of interactions among organisms.

▶ Adapting to the Environment *(page 594)*

Match the term with its definition.

Term	Definition
_____ **1.** natural selection	**a.** Characteristic that allows a species to live successfully in its environment
_____ **2.** adaptation	**b.** The way a species makes its living
_____ **3.** niche	**c.** Process in which a species becomes better suited to its environment

▶ Competition *(page 595)*

4. Is the following sentence true or false? The struggle between organisms to survive in a habitat with limited resources is called natural selection.

_____

5. Is the following sentence true or false? Specializing can reduce

competition. _____

▶ Predation (pages 596–598)

6. An interaction in which one organism kills and eats another is called

_____. The organism that does the killing is the

_____. The organism that is killed is the _____.

7. Is the following sentence true or false? If a prey population decreases, the

population of its predator probably will decrease as well. _____

▶ Symbiosis (pages 599–600)

8. Complete the compare/contrast table.

Types of Symbiotic Relationships	
Type of Relationship	**How Species Are Affected**
Mutualism	
	One species benefits; the other species is unharmed.
	One species benefits; the other species is harmed.

9. In a parasitic relationship, the organism that benefits is called a(n)

_____, and the organism it lives on or in is called a(n)

_____.

📖 Reading Skill Practice

When you read about related concepts, making a compare/contrast table can help you focus on their similarities and differences. Make a table comparing and contrasting the three major types of interactions among organisms in Section 18-3. For more information on compare/contrast tables, see page 720 in the Skills Handbook of your textbook. Do your work on a separate sheet of paper.

© Prentice-Hall, Inc.

CHAPTER 18, Populations and Communities (continued)

WordWise

Use the clues to make a list of key terms from Chapter 18. Then find and circle each of the key terms in the hidden-word puzzle. The terms may be written across or down.

Clues	Key Terms
Organism that is harmed in parasitism	_____
Struggle between organisms for limited resources in a habitat	_____
Organism that does the killing in predation	_____
Organism that is killed in predation	_____
All the living and nonliving things that interact in an area	_____
Place where an organism lives and that provides for its needs	_____
Organism that benefits in parasitism	_____
Interaction in which one organism kills and eats another	_____
Study of how living things interact with each other and their environment	_____
An approximation of a number	_____
Relationship in which one species benefits and one is unharmed	_____
A group of similar organisms that can produce fertile offspring	_____
An organism's particular role in an ecosystem	_____
Relationship in which at least one species benefits	_____

```
c  a  p  t  d  a  a  t  o  n  i  s
o  e  f  g  n  p  h  o  s  t  s  p
m  e  s  t  i  m  a  t  e  s  i  r
m  c  p  p  c  o  b  l  c  y  p  p
e  o  e  a  h  y  i  o  o  m  r  r
n  s  c  r  e  x  t  g  l  b  e  e
s  y  i  a  w  c  a  y  o  i  d  d
a  s  e  s  d  m  t  c  g  o  a  a
l  t  s  i  p  r  e  y  y  s  t  t
i  e  n  t  r  e  y  e  p  i  o  i
s  m  t  e  e  y  p  r  o  s  r  o
m  c  o  m  p  e  t  i  t  i  o  n
```

Science Explorer *Focus on Earth Science*

CHAPTER 19

Ecosystems and Biomes

....

Energy Flow in Ecosystems
(pages 606–612)

This section explains the different roles that organisms play in the movement of energy through an ecosystem. The section also describes how organisms in the different roles interact to form food chains and food webs.

▶ **Energy Roles** (pages 607–609)

Match the energy role with its definition.

Energy Role	Definition
_____ 1. producer	**a.** Organism that breaks down wastes and dead organisms
_____ 2. consumer	**b.** Organism that obtains energy by feeding on other organisms
_____ 3. decomposer	**c.** Organism that can make its own food

4. What types of organisms are producers? _____

   _____

   _____

5. Is the following sentence true or false? Energy enters all ecosystems as

   sunlight. _____

6. Is the following sentence true or false? Producers are the source of all the

   food in an ecosystem. _____

7. List two major groups of decomposers.

   a. _____   b. _____

CHAPTER 19, Ecosystems and Biomes (continued)

8. Complete the compare/contrast table.

Types of Consumers	
Type of Consumer	**Type of Food**
	Only plants
Carnivore	
	Both plants and animals
	Dead organisms

9. Is the following sentence true or false? Decomposers return raw

materials to the environment. _____

▶ Food Chains and Food Webs (pages 609–611)

10. A series of events in which one organism eats another and obtains

energy is called a(n) _____.

11. Label the producer and the first-level and second-level consumers in
the food chain.

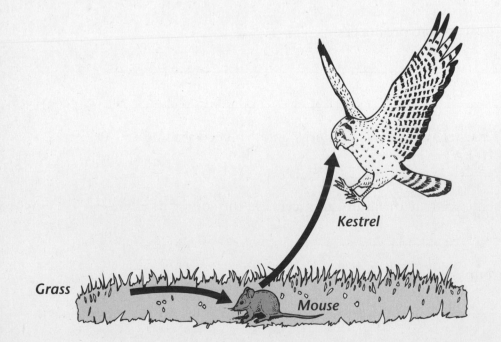

Kestrel

Grass   *Mouse*

12. The many overlapping food chains in an ecosystem make up a(n)

_____.

13. Circle the letter of each sentence that is true about a food web.

    a. Producers are at the top of the food web.

    b. All first-level consumers are carnivores.

    c. Second-level consumers may be carnivores or omnivores.

    d. An organism may play more than one role in a food web.

▶ Energy Pyramids (pages 611–612)

14. What does an energy pyramid show? _____

_____

15. Circle the letter of each sentence that is true about an energy pyramid.

    a. The greatest amount of energy is available at the producer level.

    b. At each level of the pyramid, there is more energy available.

    c. About half the energy at one level is transferred to the next.

    d. Most food webs have only three or four feeding levels.

16. Why are there usually few organisms at the top of a food web?

_____

_____

_____

SECTION 19-2 Cycles of Matter (pages 613–617)

This section describes three cycles in nature that recycle matter in ecosystems.

▶ Recycling Matter (pages 613–614)

1. Matter is made up of tiny particles called _____.
Combinations of two or more of these tiny particles are called

_____.

CHAPTER 19, Ecosystems and Biomes *(continued)*

2. Circle the letter of each sentence that is true about matter and energy in ecosystems.

   a. The supply of matter in an ecosystem is limited.

   b. Matter is recycled in an ecosystem.

   c. Energy is recycled in an ecosystem.

   d. Energy must be supplied constantly to an ecosystem.

▶ The Water Cycle (pages 614–615)

3. Is the following sentence true or false? Water is the most common compound in all living cells on Earth. _____

4. The continuous process by which water moves from Earth's surface to the atmosphere and back is the _____.

Match the term with its definition.

Term	Definition
_____ **5.** evaporation	**a.** Process by which liquid water changes to water vapor
_____ **6.** condensation	**b.** Forms of water that fall from clouds and reach Earth's surface
_____ **7.** precipitation	**c.** Process by which water vapor changes to liquid water

8. Is the following sentence true or false? The energy for evaporation comes from the sun. _____

9. What process results in the formation of clouds? _____

   _____

   _____

10. List four forms of precipitation.

    a. _____ **b.** _____ **c.** _____ **d.** _____

▶ The Carbon and Oxygen Cycles (pages 615–616)

11. Is the following sentence true or false? Carbon dioxide is not necessary

for life. _____

12. Circle the letter of each sentence that is true about the carbon and oxygen cycles.

    a. Producers take in oxygen during photosynthesis.

    b. Producers release carbon dioxide as a result of photosynthesis.

    c. Consumers release carbon dioxide as a waste product.

    d. Consumers take in oxygen for their life processes.

13. Label the arrows to indicate whether they show the movement of oxygen or the movement of carbon dioxide through the ecosystem.

▶ The Nitrogen Cycle (pages 616–617)

14. Is the following sentence true or false? Most organisms use nitrogen

directly from the air. _____

15. The process of changing free nitrogen gas into a usable form of

nitrogen is called _____.

16. Is the following sentence true or false? Most nitrogen fixation is

performed by plants. _____

CHAPTER 19, Ecosystems and Biomes (continued)

 **Reading Skill Practice**

When you read about a complex process, studying a diagram of the process may help you understand it better. Study the diagram of the nitrogen cycle in Figure 10 of Section 19-2. Summarize the steps in the cycle in your own words. Do your work on a separate sheet of paper.

· ·

SECTION 19-3 Biogeography (pages 618-621)

This section describes why organisms are found where they are and how organisms can move from one place to another. The section also describes factors that limit the movement of organisms from place to place.

▶ Introduction (page 618)

1. The study of where organisms live is called _____.

▶ Continental Drift (pages 618–619)

2. What is continental drift? _____

_____

_____

3. Is the following sentence true or false? All the continents were together

   in one large continent about 225 million years ago. _____

4. Is the following sentence true or false? The movement of the continents

   has had little impact on the distribution of species. _____

▶ Means of Dispersal (pages 619–620)

5. The movement of organisms from one place to another is called

   _____.

Science Explorer *Focus on Earth Science*

6. Complete the concept map.

7. What organisms are dispersed by the wind? _____

_____

_____

8. Give examples of ways organisms may be dispersed by other living things.

_____

_____

_____

_____

9. Is the following sentence true or false? Humans are not important to

the dispersal of other species. _____

10. Species that have naturally evolved in an area are called

_____. Species that have been carried into a new locale

by people are called _____.

▶ **Limits to Dispersal** (pages 620–621)

11. List three factors that limit dispersal of a species.

a. _____ b. _____ c. _____

12. What are some examples of physical barriers that limit dispersal?

_____

_____

CHAPTER 19, Ecosystems and Biomes *(continued)*

13. How can competition act as a barrier to dispersal? _____

_____

_____

14. The typical weather pattern in an area over a long period of time is the

area's _____.

15. Is the following sentence true or false? Places with similar climates tend

to have similar niches for species to occupy. _____

....

SECTION 19–4 **Earth's Biomes** (pages 624–635)

This section describes several different biomes, or groups of similar ecosystems, that are found on planet Earth. The section also tells where the different biomes are located.

▶ **Introduction** (page 624)

1. A group of ecosystems with similar climates and organisms is called

a(n) _____.

2. Is the following sentence true or false? It is mostly the climate

conditions in an area that determine its biome. _____

▶ **Rain Forest Biomes** (pages 625–626)

3. Circle the letter of each sentence that is true about tropical rain forests.

a. They are found only in Africa and South America.

b. They receive a lot of rainfall and sunlight year-round.

c. They contain a limited number of species.

d. They are much warmer in some seasons than in others.

4. The tall trees in a tropical rain forest form a leafy roof called the

_____.

5. How do temperate rain forests differ from tropical rain forests?

_____

_____

6. Where are temperate rain forests located? _____

_____

▶ Desert Biomes (pages 626–627)

7. Circle the letter of each sentence that is true about deserts.

   a. They receive less than 10 centimeters of rain per year.

   b. They have more evaporation than precipitation.

   c. They are always hot.

   d. They have extreme temperatures.

▶ Grassland Biomes (pages 627–628)

8. Circle the letter of each sentence that is true about grasslands.

   a. They have many trees.

   b. They have rich soil.

   c. They receive more than 75 centimeters of rain each year.

   d. They are home to many of the largest animals on Earth.

9. Grasslands that are located closer to the equator than prairies are called

   _____ .

▶ Deciduous Forest Biomes (pages 628–629)

10. Trees that shed their leaves and grow new ones each year are called

   _____ .

11. Circle the letter of the sentence that is true about deciduous forests.

   a. They receive at least 50 centimeters of rain each year.

   b. Their temperatures are constant throughout the year.

   c. Their growing season usually lasts for 10 months.

   d. They contain very few habitats.

CHAPTER 19, Ecosystems and Biomes (continued)

▶ Boreal Forest Biomes (pages 629–630)

12. What type of trees are found in a boreal forest? _____

_____

13. Circle the letter of each sentence that is true about boreal forests.

   a. They are farther north than deciduous forests.

   b. They have very cold winters.

   c. They receive little snow.

   d. Their most common species of trees are fir, spruce, and hemlock.

▶ Tundra Biomes (pages 630–631)

14. An extremely cold, dry, land biome is the _____.

15. Circle the letter of each sentence that is true about the tundra.

   a. It may receive no more precipitation than a desert.

   b. Most of its soil is frozen all year.

   c. Its plants include mosses and dwarf trees.

   d. Its only animals are insects and birds.

▶ Mountains and Ice (page 631)

16. Is the following sentence true or false? If you hiked to the top of a tall

    mountain, you would pass through a series of biomes. _____

17. What are some organisms adapted to life on the ice? _____

_____

▶ Freshwater Biomes (pages 632–633)

18. Circle the letter of each sentence that is true about water biomes.

   a. They cover about one quarter of Earth's surface.

   b. They include both freshwater and saltwater biomes.

   c. They are affected by temperature, sunlight, oxygen, and salt content.

   d. Their most common producers are plants.

19. Is the following sentence true or false? Lakes are generally larger and

deeper than ponds. _____

20. Complete the Venn diagram.

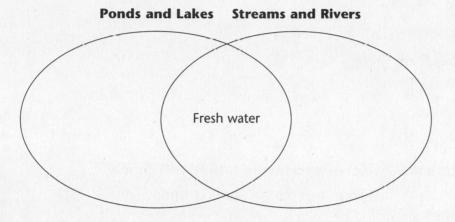

Ponds and Lakes   Streams and Rivers

Fresh water

▶ Marine Biomes (pages 633–635)

21. Complete the compare/contrast table.

Types of Marine Biomes	
Type of Biome	**Where It Is Located**
Estuary	Where fresh river water and salty ocean water meet
	Between the highest and lowest tide
	Below the low-tide line and out over the continental shelf
	On the surface of the open ocean
	Below the surface of the open ocean

22. Is the following sentence true or false? An estuary is a very poor habitat

for living things. _____

23. Why is the intertidal zone a difficult place to live? _____

_____

_____

_____

CHAPTER 19, Ecosystems and Biomes *(continued)*

24. Circle the letter of each sentence that is true about the neritic zone.

    a. Its water is too deep for photosynthesis to occur.

    b. It is particularly rich in living things.

    c. Many large schools of fish feed there.

    d. Coral reefs may form there.

25. Is the following sentence true or false? Algae form the basis of almost

all open-ocean food webs. _____

26. Circle the letter of each sentence that is true about the deep zone.

    a. Throughout most of the deep zone, the ocean is completely dark.

    b. Most animals in the deep zone feed on algae.

    c. Some animals in the deep zone glow in the dark.

    d. Plants grow on the ocean floor in the deep zone.

SECTION 19-5 Succession (pages 638-640)

This section describes a series of predictable changes that occur in a community over time.

▶ Introduction (page 638)

1. What is succession? _____

_____

_____

▶ Primary Succession (page 639)

2. What is primary succession? _____

_____

_____

_____

3. Circle the letter of each choice that describes an area where primary succession might occur.

    a. A new island formed by the eruption of an undersea volcano

    b. An area of bare rock uncovered by a melting ice sheet

    c. A clearing in a forest left by cutting down the trees

    d. An area without any trees or other plants following a forest fire

4. The first species to populate the area in primary succession are called

    _____.

5. Primary species are often _____ and _____.

6. How do pioneer species help develop soil? _____

    _____

    _____

    _____

▶ Secondary Succession (page 640)

7. The series of changes that occur after a disturbance in an existing

    ecosystem is called _____.

8. What natural disturbances can result in secondary succession? _____

    _____

    _____

9. What human activities can result in secondary succession? _____

    _____

    _____

10. Is the following sentence true or false? Secondary succession occurs

    more slowly than primary succession. _____

11. The particular species that come and go in the process of succession

    depend on the _____.

CHAPTER 19, Ecosystems and Biomes *(continued)*

WordWise

Match each definition in the left column with the correct term in the right column. Then write the number of each term in the appropriate box below. When you have filled all the boxes, add up the numbers in each column, row, and two diagonals. All the sums should be the same.

Definitions

A. Consumer that eats both plants and animals

B. Carnivore that feeds on the bodies of dead organisms

C. Process by which a liquid changes to a gas

D. Bumps on the roots of certain plants that house nitrogen-fixing bacteria

E. Movement of organisms from one place to another

F. Average conditions of temperature, precipitation, winds, and clouds in an area

G. Group of ecosystems with similar climates and organisms

H. Permanently frozen soil found in the tundra climate region

I. Series of predictable changes that occur in a community over time

Terms

1. scavenger
2. biome
3. climate
4. succession
5. dispersal
6. omnivore
7. nodules
8. evaporation
9. permafrost

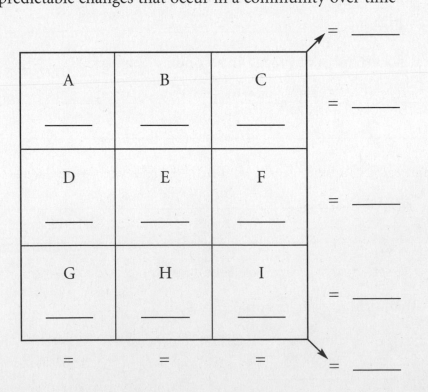

Science Explorer *Focus on Earth Science*

CHAPTER 20
LIVING RESOURCES

· ·

SECTION 20-1 Environmental Issues (pages 646-651)

This section describes three main types of environmental issues and three different approaches to resolving them. The section also describes how lawmakers weigh the costs and benefits of proposals to deal with environmental issues.

▶ Types of Environmental Issues (pages 646–647)

1. Complete the concept map.

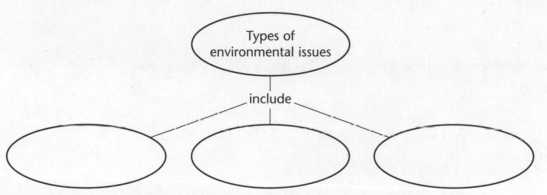

Match the term with its definition.

Term	Definition
_____ **2.** natural resource	**a.** Resources that are not replaced as they are used
_____ **3.** renewable resource	**b.** Resources that are naturally replaced in a relatively short time
_____ **4.** nonrenewable resource	**c.** Anything in the environment that is used by people

5. Circle the letter of the sentence that is true about the human population.

   a. It grew rapidly until A.D. 1650.   **b.** It grew slowly until A.D. 1950.

   c. It was 6 billion by A.D. 2000.   **d.** It was 1 billion in A.D. 1000.

CHAPTER 20, **Living Resources** *(continued)*

6. Why did the human population grow so rapidly in recent centuries?

_____

_____

_____

_____

7. Any change to the environment that has a negative effect on living

things is called _____.

8. What are some human activities that result in pollution? _____

_____

_____

_____

▶ Approaches to Environmental Issues (pages 648–650)

9. The study of the natural processes that occur in the environment and

how humans can affect them is called _____.

10. Complete the compare/contrast table.

Approaches to Environmental Issues	
Approach	**Viewpoint**
	The environment should be exploited for its resources.
	The environment should not be disturbed for people's benefit.
	The environment and its resources should be managed for the future.

▶ Weighing Costs and Benefits (page 651)

11. Is the following sentence true or false? Costs and benefits are measured

only in terms of money. _____

12. Circle the letter of each choice that would be a cost of drilling for oil in Antarctica.

    a. Transporting the oil

    b. Risk of oil spills

    c. Many new jobs

    d. Potential harm to sea animals

· ·

SECTION 20-2 **Forests and Fisheries** (pages 653-657)

This section describes resources that come from forests and from areas of the ocean called fisheries. The section also explains how forests and fisheries are managed to protect them for future use.

▶ **Forest Resources** (page 653)

1. What are some valuable materials or products provided by forests?

_____

_____

_____

2. Circle the letter of each sentence that is a reason people benefit from trees.

    a. Trees produce carbon dioxide.

    b. Trees absorb pollutants.

    c. Trees help prevent flooding.

    d. Trees help control soil erosion.

▶ **Managing Forests** (pages 654-655)

3. Is the following sentence true or false? Nearly a third of the area of the United States is covered with forests. _____

4. Is the following sentence true or false? Forests are a nonrenewable resource. _____

CHAPTER 20, Living Resources *(continued)*

5. Complete the Venn diagram.

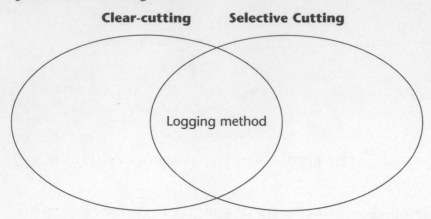

Clear-cutting   **Selective Cutting**

Logging method

6. Complete the compare/contrast table.

Advantages and Disadvantages of Different Logging Methods		
Logging Method	**Advantages**	**Disadvantages**
	Quicker, cheaper, safer	Exposes soil to erosion
	Less damaging to habitat	Can be dangerous to loggers

7. A regular amount of a renewable resource that can be harvested

without reducing the future supply is called a(n) _____.

8. How can forests provide a sustainable yield? _____

_____

_____

9. What is certified wood? _____

_____

_____

▶ Fisheries (pages 656–657)

10. An area with a large population of valuable ocean organisms is called

a(n) _____.

© Prentice-Hall, Inc.

11. Is the following sentence true or false? Scientists estimate that 50 percent of the world's major fisheries have been overfished.

_____

Match the approach to managing fisheries with its example.

Approach	Example
_____ **12.** fishing limits	**a.** Requiring the use of nets that allow young fish to escape
_____ **13.** fishing methods	**b.** Introducing unusual species of fish as food
_____ **14.** aquaculture	**c.** Setting an upper limit on the amount of fish that can be caught
_____ **15.** new resources	**d.** Raising fish in an artificial pond

· ·

SECTION 20-3 Biodiversity (pages 659-667)

This section describes factors that affect biodiversity, or the number of species in an area. The section also explains why biodiversity is valuable, how it is being threatened, and what is being done to protect it.

▶ Introduction (page 659)

1. The number of different species in an area is called its _____.

▶ Factors Affecting Biodiversity (pages 659–660)

2. Complete the concept map.

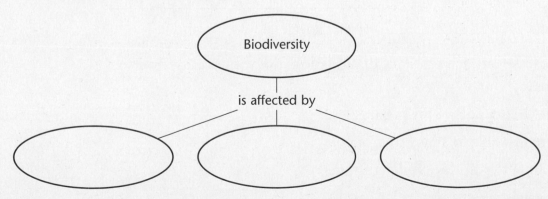

CHAPTER 20, Living Resources *(continued)*

3. Circle the letter of each sentence that is true about biodiversity.

   a. Large areas contain more species than small areas.

   b. The number of species decreases from the poles toward the equator.

   c. Tropical rain forests are the most diverse ecosystems.

   d. Coral reefs are the second most diverse ecosystems.

4. What is niche diversity? _____

   _____

   _____

▶ The Value of Biodiversity (pages 660–661)

5. Is the following sentence true or false? Biodiversity has no economic

   value. _____

6. A species that influences the survival of many other species in an

   ecosystem is called a(n) _____.

7. Is the following sentence true or false? If a keystone species disappears,

   the entire ecosystem may change. _____

▶ Gene Pool Diversity (page 662)

8. Structures in an organism's cells that carry its hereditary information are

   called _____.

9. The individual differences of genes among members of a species make

   up the total _____ of that species.

10. Circle the letter of each sentence that is true about species with diverse
    gene pools.

    a. They are better able to resist parasites.

    b. They are less able to adapt to drought.

    c. They can better tolerate fungus attacks.

    d. They are less able to survive disease.

© Prentice-Hall, Inc.

▶ Extinction of Species (pages 662–663)

11. Circle the letter of each sentence that is true about extinction.

   a. It is a natural process.

   b. Many species are now extinct.

   c. Extinctions have occurred only in the last few centuries.

   d. The number of species becoming extinct has increased dramatically.

12. Is the following sentence true or false? Once a population drops below a certain level, the species may not be able to recover. _____

13. Complete the compare/contrast table.

Extinction of Species	
Category of Species	**Status**
	Has disappeared from Earth
	Could become extinct in the near future
	Could become endangered in the near future

▶ Causes of Extinction (pages 663–665)

14. What natural events might cause extinction? _____

_____

_____

15. Is the following sentence true or false? The major cause of extinction is habitat fragmentation. _____

Match the term with its definition.

Term	Definition
_____ **16.** habitat destruction	**a.** Breaking larger habitats into smaller, isolated pieces
_____ **17.** habitat fragmentation	**b.** Illegally killing or removing wildlife species
_____ **18.** poaching	**c.** Loss of a natural habitat

CHAPTER 20, Living Resources *(continued)*

19. How can pollutants affect organisms? _____

_____

_____

▶ Protecting Biodiversity (pages 666–667)

20. The mating of animals in zoos or wildlife preserves to protect severely

endangered species is called _____.

21. Is the following sentence true or false? Laws can help protect individual

species. _____

22. Is the following sentence true or false? The most effective way to preserve

biodiversity is to protect individual species. _____

Reading Skill Practice

When you read a long section, taking notes may help you organize and remember the information. As you read or review Section 20-3, take notes by writing each heading and listing the main points under each heading. Do your work on a separate sheet of paper.

© Prentice-Hall, Inc.

SECTION 20-4 The Search for New Medicines (pages 668–670)

This section explains why biodiversity is important for medicine.

▶ Plants and Medicines (pages 668–669)

1. Is the following sentence true or false? Some chemicals produced by rain

forest plants can be used to fight human disease. _____

2. Why do plants have the ability to fight disease? _____

_____

_____

▶ The Story of Taxol (page 669)

3. What is taxol? _____

_____

4. Circle the letter of each sentence that is true about taxol.

   a. It prevents cancer cells from dividing.

   b. It causes cancer cells to grow and divide very rapidly.

   c. It shrinks certain types of tumors.

   d. It has not yet been tested in the laboratory.

▶ A Threatened Supply of Taxol (page 670)

5. Is the following sentence true or false? The demand for taxol as a cancer

treatment has grown rapidly. _____

6. Why is the supply of taxol threatened? _____

_____

_____

▶ Biodiversity and Medicine (page 670)

7. Circle the letter of each sentence that is true about biodiversity and medicine.

   a. About 50 percent of all medicines sold today contain chemicals originally found in wild organisms.

   b. About half of the world's known plant species have been studied for possible medical use.

   c. The American Medical Association has called for the protection of Earth's biodiversity.

   d. Scientists and doctors believe there are no more new medicines in nature.

CHAPTER 20, Living Resources (continued)

WordWise

Review key terms from Chapter 20 by solving the crossword puzzle.

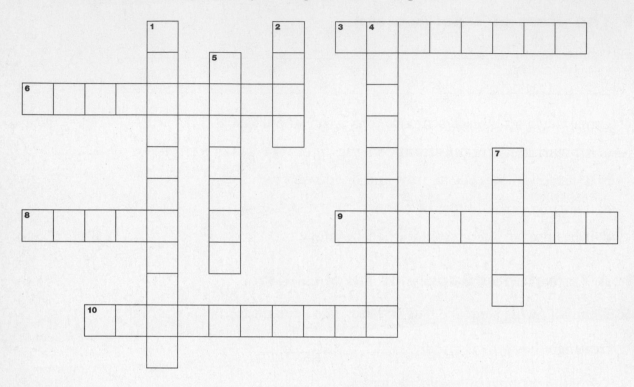

Clues down

1. Practice of raising fish and other water organisms for food
2. Structure in an organism's cells that carries its hereditary information
4. Term used to describe a species that is in danger of becoming extinct
5. Area with a large population of valuable ocean organisms
7. To hunt wildlife illegally

Clues across

3. Term used to describe a species that influences the survival of many others in an ecosystem
6. Change to the environment that has a negative effect on living things
8. Chemical in Pacific yew tree bark that has cancer-fighting properties
9. Term used to describe resources that are replaced naturally
10. Term used to describe a species that could become endangered

CHAPTER 21

ENERGY RESOURCES

··

SECTION 21–1 **Fossil Fuels** (pages 676-682)

This section explains how fuels provide energy. The section also explains what fossil fuels are and compares and contrasts the different types of fossil fuels.

▶ Fuels and Energy (pages 676–677)

1. A substance that provides a form of energy, such as heat, as a result of a

   chemical change is a(n) _____.

2. Is the following sentence true or false? Energy cannot be converted from

   one form to another. _____

3. The process of burning a fuel is called _____.

4. Is the following sentence true or false? The energy stored in fuels can be

   used to generate electricity. _____

5. Circle the letter of each sentence that is true about the production of
   electric power.

   a. In most power plants, water is boiled to make steam.

   b. The mechanical energy of steam turns the shaft of a generator.

   c. Powerful magnets turn inside a wire coil.

   d. Electricity is produced by a turbine.

▶ What Are Fossil Fuels? (page 678)

6. Energy-rich substances formed from the remains of once-living

   organisms are called _____.

CHAPTER 21, Energy Resources *(continued)*

7. List the three major fossil fuels.

a. _____ b. _____ c. _____

8. Energy-rich chemical compounds that contain carbon and hydrogen

atoms are called _____.

9. Complete the flow chart.

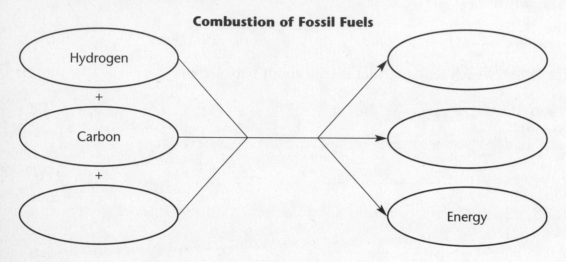

Combustion of Fossil Fuels

▶ **Coal** (pages 678–679)

10. A solid fossil fuel formed from plant remains is _____.

11. Is the following sentence true or false? Today, coal provides 23 percent

of the energy used worldwide. _____

12. Is the following sentence true or false? The major use of coal is to fuel

factories. _____

13. Known deposits of coal and other fossil fuels that can be obtained

using current technology are called _____.

14. Circle the letter of the sentence that is true about coal as an energy source.

a. It is the least plentiful fossil fuel in the United States.

b. It is difficult to transport.

c. It provides a lot of energy when burned.

d. It produces less air pollution than other fossil fuels.

© Prentice-Hall, Inc.

15. How can coal mining harm the environment? _____

_____

_____

_____

▶ Oil (pages 680–681)

16. Another name for oil—the thick, black, liquid fossil fuel—is

_____.

17. Circle the letter of each sentence that is true about petroleum.

   a. Petroleum accounts for more than half the energy produced in the world.

   b. Petroleum fuels most cars, airplanes, trains, and ships.

   c. The United States consumes a third of all the petroleum produced in the world.

   d. Three percent of the world's petroleum supply is located in the United States.

18. Scientists can use _____ to test an area for oil without drilling.

19. When oil is first pumped out of the ground, it is called _____.

20. A factory where crude oil is separated into fuels and other products by

heating is called a(n) _____.

21. Compounds that are made from oil are called _____.

▶ Natural Gas (page 681)

22. Circle the letter of each sentence that is true about natural gas.

   a. It produces a lot of energy.

   b. It produces more air pollutants than oil.

   c. It is difficult to transport.

   d. It is highly flammable.

23. Is the following sentence true or false? Because natural gas is less dense

than oil, it often rises above an oil deposit. _____

© Prentice-Hall, Inc.

CHAPTER 21, Energy Resources (continued)

▶ **Fuel Supply and Demand** (page 682)

24. Is the following sentence true or false? Fossil fuels are considered a

    renewable resource. _____

25. Circle the letter of each sentence that is true about the supply of fossil fuels.

    a. Fossil fuels take hundreds of millions of years to form.

    b. One half of Earth's known oil reserves has already been used.

    c. Most nations that consume a lot of fossil fuel have large reserves of their own.

    d. New sources of energy are needed to replace decreasing fossil fuel reserves.

· ·

SECTION 21-2 Renewable Sources of Energy (pages 683-690)

This section describes several renewable sources of energy and explains the advantages and disadvantages of each energy source.

▶ **Energy From the Sun** (pages 683–684)

1. What is solar energy? _____

2. Circle the letter of each sentence that is true about solar energy.

    a. It is the source of most other renewable energy resources.

    b. It causes pollution.

    c. It will not run out for billions of years.

    d. It is available only when the sun is shining.

▶ **Solar Technologies** (pages 684–685)

3. How do solar plants capture energy and use it to generate electricity?

    _____

    _____

    _____

4. Is the following sentence true or false? Solar energy can be converted directly into electricity in a solar cell. _____

5. What are solar cells used to power? _____

_____

_____

6. Is the following sentence true or false? Solar heating systems convert sunlight into mechanical energy. _____

7. Complete the concept map.

```
         ( Solar heating systems )
                     |
                  can be
              /            \
    (          )          (          )
```

8. How do active solar heating systems differ from passive solar heating systems? _____

_____

_____

▶ Capturing the Wind (page 686)

9. List other renewable sources of energy besides the sun.

a. _____ b. _____ c. _____

d. _____ e. _____ f. _____

10. Circle the letter of each sentence that is true about wind energy.

   a. It provides 10 percent of the world's electricity.

   b. It is the fastest-growing energy source.

   c. It causes pollution.

   d. In some places it is the major source of power.

CHAPTER 21, Energy Resources *(continued)*

11. Is the following sentence true or false? Most places have winds that blow

steadily enough to be a worthwhile energy source. _____

▶ The Power of Flowing Water (pages 686–687)

12. Electricity produced by flowing water is called _____.

13. Is the following sentence true or false? Hydroelectric power is the least widely used source of renewable energy in the world today.

_____

14. What are two limitations on hydroelectric power in the United States?

_____

_____

▶ Tidal Energy (page 687)

15. Power plants that are built to take advantage of the regular motion of

tides are called _____.

16. Circle the letter of the sentence that is true about tidal power.

    a. Tidal power can be used to generate electricity.

    b. Many tidal power plants have already been built.

    c. Most coastal areas are suitable for building tidal power plants.

    d. Tidal power will probably become a major source of energy in the future.

▶ Biomass Fuels (page 688)

17. Fuels made from living things are called _____.

18. Circle the letter of each sentence that is true about biomass fuels.

    a. They include leaves, food wastes, and manure.

    b. They can be converted to other fuels.

    c. They are widely used today in the United States.

    d. They are renewable resources.

▶ **Tapping Earth's Energy** (page 689)

19. Intense heat from Earth's interior is called _____.

20. Is the following sentence true or false? Geothermal energy is an

    unlimited source of cheap energy. _____

21. Add arrows to the drawing to show how water flows through a
    geothermal power plant.

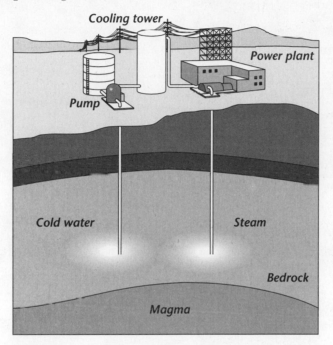

▶ **Hydrogen Power** (page 690)

22. What is the obstacle to using hydrogen as a fuel? _____

    _____

    _____

📖 **Reading Skill Practice**

When you read a long section, identifying the sentence that best expresses the main topic under
each heading can help you focus on the most important points. Identify and write the sentence
that best expresses the main topic under each heading in Section 21-2. Do your work on a
separate sheet of paper.

CHAPTER 21, Energy Resources *(continued)*

Nuclear Energy
(pages 693-697)

This section explains how nuclear reactions inside atoms can produce energy. The section also describes the advantages and disadvantages of nuclear energy.

▶ Introduction (page 693)

1. The central core of an atom that contains the protons and neutrons is

   called the _____.

2. Complete the concept map.

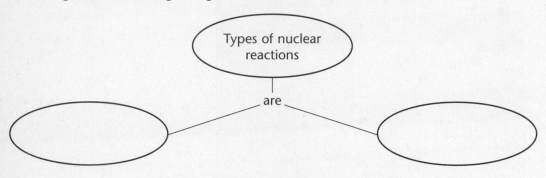

▶ Fission Reactions and Energy (pages 693–694)

3. Is the following sentence true or false? Nuclear reactions convert matter

   into energy. _____

4. What formula, developed by Albert Einstein, describes the relationship

   between energy and matter? _____

5. The splitting of an atom's nucleus into two smaller nuclei is called

   _____.

6. Circle the letter of each sentence that is true about nuclear fission.

   a. It uses uranium as a fuel.

   b. It is a chain reaction.

   c. It is extremely safe.

   d. It can generate electricity.

Science Explorer *Focus on Earth Science*

▶ Nuclear Power Plants (pages 694–695)

7. How is electricity produced in a nuclear power plant? _____

_____

_____

_____

Match the part of a nuclear reactor with its function.

Part of Reactor

_____ 8. reactor vessel

_____ 9. fuel rod

_____ 10. control rod

_____ 11. heat exchanger

Function

a. It contains the uranium.

b. It is where nuclear fission occurs.

c. It changes hot water to steam.

d. It controls the reactions.

▶ The Risks of Nuclear Fission (pages 695–696)

12. When fuel rods in a nuclear power plant generate so much heat that

they start to melt, the condition is called a(n) _____.

13. Why is it difficult to dispose of radioactive wastes produced by power

plants? _____

_____

▶ The Quest to Control Fusion (pages 696–697)

14. The combining of two atomic nuclei to produce a single larger nucleus

is called _____.

15. Circle the letter of each sentence that is true about nuclear fusion.

a. It produces less energy per atom than nuclear fission.

b. The fuel it needs is readily available.

c. Scientists have not yet been able to control a large-scale fusion
reaction.

d. It is widely used today to produce electricity.

CHAPTER 21, Energy Resources *(continued)*

• •

SECTION 21–4 **Energy Conservation**
(pages 699–702)

This section describes several ways that energy use can be reduced to make available fuels last as long as possible.

▶ **Introduction** (page 699)

1. What are two approaches to the problem of the limited supply of fossil

   fuels? _____

   _____

   _____

   _____

▶ **Conservation and Efficiency** (pages 699–702)

2. Reducing energy use is called _____.

3. The percentage of energy from a fuel that is actually used to perform

   work is its _____.

4. What happens to the energy from a fuel that is not used to perform work?

   _____

   _____

5. Is the following sentence true or false? Incandescent light bulbs waste

   less energy than compact fluorescent bulbs. _____

6. A layer of material that helps block the transfer of heat between the air

   inside and outside a building is called _____.

7. How does insulation work? _____

   _____

   _____

Science Explorer *Focus on Earth Science*

8. Circle the letter of the choice that is the best material for insulation.

    a. fiberglass   **b.** brick   **c.** stone   **d.** glass

9. Why do new windows have two panes of glass with space between them?

_____

_____

_____

10. How have engineers improved the energy efficiency of cars?

_____

_____

11. What are some ways to reduce the number of cars on the road?

_____

_____

_____

_____

12. Is the following sentence true or false? A car that runs on electricity is less

energy-efficient than one that runs directly on fuel. _____

▶ What You Can Do (page 702)

13. Circle the letter of each sentence that describes a way you can reduce your personal energy use.

    a. Use air conditioners instead of fans.

    b. Use electric lights whenever possible.

    c. Ride buses and trains.

    d. Keep your home warmer in winter and cooler in summer.

14. Why does recycling aluminum help to save energy? _____

_____

_____

CHAPTER 21, Energy Resources (continued)

WordWise

Solve the clues by filling in the blanks with key terms from Chapter 21. Then write the numbered letters in the correct order to find the hidden message.

Clues   **Key Terms**

Substance that provides energy as the   _ _ _ _
result of a chemical change   1 2

Compound made from oil   _ _ _ _ _ _ _ _ _ _ _ _
                                               3   4

Liquid fossil fuel   _ _ _ _ _ _ _
                                               5   6 7

A known deposit of fuels   _ _ _ _ _ _ _
                                                        8

Factory where crude oil is separated into   _ _ _ _ _ _
fuels and other products   9

Dangerous condition caused by   _ _ _ _ _ _ _
overheating inside a nuclear reactor   10

Percentage of energy that is used by a   _ _ _ _ _ _ _ _ _ _
device to perform work   11

Building material that blocks heat transfer   _ _ _ _ _ _ _ _ _
between the air inside and outside   12

Reducing energy use   _ _ _ _ _ _ _ _ _ _ _
                                                       13   14

Electricity produced by the kinetic   _ _ _ _ _ _ _ _ _ _ _ _
energy of moving water   15   16

Mixture of gasoline and alcohol   _ _ _ _ _ _ _
                                               17

Compound that contains carbon   _ _ _ _ _ _ _ _ _ _ _
and hydrogen atoms   18

Hidden Message

_ _ _ _   _ _ _ _ _ _ _ _   _ _ _ _ _ _ .
1 2 3 4   5 6 7 8 9 10 11 12   13 14 15 16 17 18

© Prentice-Hall, Inc.